Kathy Ann

KINDERGARTNER

Kathy Ann

KINDERGARTNER

Frances Dunlap Heron

Illustrated by JANET SMALLEY

Nashville • **ABINGDON PRESS** • *New York*

KATHY ANN KINDERGARTNER

Copyright MCMLV by Pierce & Washabaugh

ISBN 0-687-20731-2
Library of Congress Catalog Card Number: 55-6763

SET UP, PRINTED, AND BOUND BY THE
PARTHENON PRESS, AT NASHVILLE,
TENNESSEE, UNITED STATES OF AMERICA

To

SUE

AL

FRAN

DON

who taught their mother about kindergartners

Hello!

My name is Kathy Ann Quick. What's yours?

When my mother was a little girl, she wrote a book called *Betty Ann, Beginner.* It told about her going to Sunday school. Once the teacher put Mommy's new coat on the radiator, and it got knocked off and somebody stepped on it.

The teachers who read about Mommy's Sunday school tried to make their Sunday schools nice places where little girls' coats didn't fall off radiators.

You can't buy Mommy's book any more, so I decided that I would write a book. I'll tell about my Sunday school. Mrs. Heron will help me, like she did Mommy. Only she wasn't Mrs. Heron then. She was just Frances Dunlap, and she didn't have any children. Now she has four—and one of them is married to a girl named Betty Ann!

I'm changing to a different Sunday school 'cause we've just moved out here from the city. You call it a "suburb." The name of our town is Rose Park. I asked Daddy where are the roses. He said he guessed they must be in the old part of town. We live in the new part.

My daddy's name is Paul. He is a lawyer. Whenever I

7

say, "Prove it!" Mommy says, "Just like your daddy!" We have fun at our house.

My mother met my daddy at college. She worked on a newspaper for one year, and then they got married. I want to be like my mother when I grow up.

My little brother Lowell is two and a half years old. He's named that 'cause my mother's name used to be Betty Ann Lowell. Most of the time I like him, but sometimes he gets in my way.

I'm four and a half years old. My birthday is the twenty-third of April. I'm not old enough to go to everyday school, but I can go to kindergarten at Sunday school.

I'll be glad when Sunday comes. I liked Sunday school where we used to live. Mommy says I'll find new friends 'cause hundreds of people are moving to Rose Park. I already know two. Joyce is my girl friend, and Chucky is my boy friend. They live on my street.

Good-by till next Sunday.

Kathy Ann

P. S.

May I join Kathy Ann in hoping that her story will help parents, teachers, and church leaders understand how a kindergartner develops a Christian attitude toward life, and particularly how the church school, working with the home, can best nurture that development. If adults can but see through the child's eye the effects of what they do, and what they so often neglect to do, many of their problems about "techniques" will vanish. On the other hand, if Kathy Ann sometimes seems a bit precocious in her observations, remember that she's like children in your family—"advanced for her age"!

FRANCES DUNLAP HERON

Contents

1 MARIBEL ISN'T GLAD

When we got to church this morning, my mother said to a man in front, "Will you please tell us where the kindergarten meets?"

The man said, "Go down those steps and ask somebody."

We started downstairs. We met a woman and Mommy asked her, "Is the kindergarten room down here?" And the woman said, "I don't know much about the basement. I teach upstairs."

We heard a crying noise, and Mommy went that way. And there by the furnace was the kindergarten. The little girl who was crying was holding on to her mother and saying, "No, no, no!"

The teacher saw us by the door, and I heard her say, "Oh, my, another one!"

She walked over and said, "How old is she?"

I can talk myself. I told her, "I'm four and a half."

Mommy asked if there was a place for Lowell, and she said there wasn't any nursery department 'cause there wasn't any room. All the new people moving out to Rose Park are just pushing the sides of the church out. But I looked, and the sides are still there.

"I-just-don't-know-where-we're-going-to-put-everybody-what's-your-name-honey?" She talked in a big hurry.

I said, "Kathy Ann Quick. What's your name?"

Her mouth went open. She said, "Mrs. Turnip" or something like that. It's funny, grownups always ask me how old I am and what is my name, but they don't tell me their names. Or they talk so I can't understand them.

Mrs. Turnip set me on a chair with Ellen. I wanted a chair of my own, but there wasn't any. The chair was at a table. My feet wouldn't touch the floor.

I didn't know Ellen. Chucky came in, and he waved at

11

me and wanted me to sit at his table. But Mrs. Turnip told us to stay where we were or we'd get our wraps mixed up. We had to hang wraps on the backs of our chairs.

We sat some more. Mrs. Turnip said we'd start Sunday school as soon as Miss Cora came to play the piano. But Miss Cora didn't come. So Mrs. Turnip asked the mothers could any of them play the piano.

My mother could. She put Lowell on a chair with somebody close to Chucky.

Mrs. Turnip couldn't find the "sunshine song," so we sang "Jesus Loves Me." Everywhere I go to Sunday school, they sing "Jesus Loves Me." I think it's the only song some teachers know.

Mrs. Turnip said, "We're so glad to come to our nice church, aren't we?" The crying girl's mother pushed her on a chair and said, "Yes, Maribel, you will stay too!" and spanked her leg.

Then Mrs. Turnip called all our names. She told us to say "Here" real loud. Every time she called a name, Chucky said, "What a stupid name!" and we all laughed. She called one name "Waldo." I never heard Waldo before. One of

the mothers kept going "Sh-h-h!" It took so long to call names I got tired.

When Mrs. Turnip finished the names, a boy came in. She said, "Find a chair with somebody, Waldo."

It was Waldo. He was late.

Mrs. Turnip gave us papers to take home. Only the new ones haven't come yet. The picture in mine is a Christmas tree. This isn't Christmas!

Mrs. Turnip told Mommy she didn't want to be the kindergarten teacher, but there wasn't anybody else. The woman who was teacher for a long time—I guess a hundred years—is sick and can't do it any more.

2 | "REPEAT-AFTER-ME"

When I got ready for Sunday school this morning, Lowell cried. He always wants to go where I go. Daddy said why not let him go. And Mommy said to Daddy, "Then you come too." So we all went to Sunday school.

Mrs. Turnip let Lowell stay with me. Only her name isn't Mrs. Turnip. Mommy found out it's Mrs. Turner. Lowell and I each one had a chair by ourselves! There's more room now 'cause the children in first grade go to another class. You call it pro-moted. Mrs. Turner said thank-goodness-she-got-rid-of-them.

Miss Cora was there today to play the piano and to help Mrs. Turner. Maribel, the crying girl, cried some more. Miss Cora said, "A big girl like you shouldn't cry."

Maribel's mother pointed to Lowell—"Look at that little boy. He isn't even three years old, and *he's* not crying."

I don't like it when people say that to me. Maribel didn't like it either. She kicked Lowell's chair.

Mrs. Turner tried to make her hold the "collection"—

13

that's the basket to put money in. Maribel didn't want to. Then Mrs. Turner looked at me and said, "You hold it, little-girl-in-the-yellow-dress." I didn't want to either. I told her my name last Sunday!

Mrs. Turner asked, "Who knows the memory verse?" Nobody did.

Mrs. Turner told us, "Repeat-after-me."

She said, "I was glad—"

We said, "I was glad—"

She said, "when they said—"

We said, "when they said—"

She said, "unto me—"

Isn't "unto" a funny word? The rest was about the house of the Lord. I wonder where that is.

Miss Cora played the sunshine song, and we stood up by the tables to be trees. We were so close together our arms got all mixed up, and we laughed. We nodded our heads for the part about "flowers are gayly blooming."

Chucky said, "Our flowers are dying." But Mrs. Turner didn't listen to him. She wanted us to listen to her. "Everybody be quiet and we'll have our lesson."

The story—that's what she means when she says "lesson" —was about a boy who went to church, only it wasn't like our church. They had toys to play with! Waldo came in while Mrs. Turner was reading the story. He pushed into me trying to find a chair.

Mrs. Turner calls it a "coloring time" after the story. Peter told her he didn't feel like coloring, but she said it was the time for it. She said, "Draw me a nice picture of a church." Peter said he didn't know how, so she said draw anything we wanted to.

I drew a watermelon. Then I put a head and two feet on and made a man. Miss Cora couldn't guess what our

14

pictures were. "What's that?" she kept asking, and then she'd say, "That's-nice-that's-nice" whether it was nice or not.

Lowell and the other littlest ones just made marks. Ellen told us to look how terrible Joyce's dog picture was. We all said it was terrible. Joyce nearly cried.

Maribel didn't cry when she drew a picture. You know what, hers was the best of anybody's! But Mrs. Turner wouldn't look at it—she said Maribel might yell if she went near her.

My hands got tired. The crayons weren't big like the ones I have at home. My arms got tired trying to reach up and work on the table. It's too high.

3 IT WASN'T JESUS

I took a little Halloween pumpkin to Sunday school today. Mommy thought maybe Mrs. Turner would let me show it. When Mommy was my age, her teacher liked to have her bring things. But Mrs. Turner just said, "Isn't-that-nice" and set it on top of the piano. She didn't say anything more about it.

Today we paid at the door. Miss Cora stood by the basket saying, "Put-your-pennies-in-put-your-pennies-in." Why do they say "pennies"? I had a dime. Miss Cora let me put it in.

Mrs. Turner said, "Who can tell us what we do with our pennies? Hold up your hands." So we all held up hands. Mrs. Turner asked Joyce. But Joyce didn't know. Mrs. Turner asked Ellen. But Ellen didn't know. Mrs. Turner asked me. But I didn't know. I just like to hold up my hand.

Mrs. Turner told us—we give our pennies to Jesus. Then she sang a Halloween song. The name of it was Doc's something or other. I couldn't tell most of the words, but I knew the last ones—"holy ghost." I guess his sheet was old and had holes in it.

We made a little church. I mean Miss Cora made it. She said cutting was too hard for us and paste was too messy. All I did was color one piece of a tree. I sat on my chair and swang my legs and looked around. I saw a man come get our money. It wasn't Jesus. It was Joyce's daddy.

The mothers sat and talked about us. They talked about me once. One said, "Doesn't that little girl have pretty blue eyes?" The other said, "Pretty brown hair too." I felt funny. I looked at the floor. I wish mothers would go to a class of their own, like Mommy does.

4 DUSTY CAKE

I'll be glad when it's Thanksgiving. Then we're going to my Grandmother Lowell's house. My Aunt Sue and Uncle Ralph and Uncle Dick and Aunt Jean will be there too. And Keith and Janet—they're my cousins.

This morning at Sunday school Mrs. Turner asked, "What day is coming?" Hughy said his birthday. He did have his birthday pennies in his pocket. But Mrs. Turner meant Thanksgiving.

She asked what do we all eat on Thanksgiving. We said turkey. All but Ellen—they eat goose. Nobody knew what else we do on Thanksgiving.

Mrs. Turner told us. You give things to poor people. Poor people don't have pretty dresses and coats like we have. They don't live in nice houses like we do in Rose Park. They don't have turkey for Thanksgiving.

So we'll give them a basket of food. Each one bring a can next Sunday. Just anything.

For Hughy's birthday Miss Cora got a cake from behind the piano. I asked could we have a piece to eat. Then I saw it was just a pan turned upside down to look like a cake. And it was dusty. The candles wouldn't stand up straight. Miss Cora lighted them. Chucky tried to help, and he burned his finger.

Hughy put his pennies in a kitty-cat bank. We counted them—one, two, three, four. I wonder what happens to the pennies now? Hughy blew out his candles, and Mrs. Turner gave them to him to take home.

Peter said he had a birthday. Miss Cora thought he already had his birthday. Peter had pennies, and he wouldn't put them in the basket. He wanted to put them in the kitty-cat bank.

So Peter burned candles too. But Miss Cora kept saying she was sure his birthday was July.

You know what, while we were singing our good-by song, the teachers weren't watching and Hughy went out the door. I saw him. Mrs. Turner told us to wait for our mothers and daddies.

When Hughy's mother came for him, he wasn't there.

She asked where was he. Mrs. Turner looked. I told her Hughy went home.

Hughy's mother talked loud like mothers do when they're mad. She said Hughy shouldn't cross the street by himself.

Then Hughy came back to our room and found his mother. He showed her his happy-birthday candles. His mother told him he was a bad boy.

5 "FOR THE POOR CHILDREN"

I don't like canned applesauce. We had it for breakfast. Daddy said some little girls would be glad to have canned applesauce. Then I remembered about the poor children who won't have turkey for Thanksgiving.

I told Mommy I had to have a can to take to Sunday school. Mommy didn't know anything about it. She called up Joyce's mother. Joyce's mother didn't know anything about it.

So Mommy called up Mrs. Turner. And I was right! Mommy said she wished the teacher would send home a letter telling things like that.

Mommy looked in the cupboard. She couldn't find anything but a can of applesauce. Then Lowell cried. He wanted a can to take to Sunday school. Mommy found some rice and put it in a can. She tied our cans in white paper. We were late to Sunday school.

But Waldo was later.

Mrs. Turner said what good children to remember the cans! We put them in an old basket on the floor in the corner. There weren't very many cans in it. I wonder who took them to the poor children. I'm glad *I'm* not poor.

Mrs. Turner didn't talk any more about the cans or the

poor children. She talked about a big rock. People went riding in a boat, and they met some Indians. It was cold and the people were hungry. The Indians cooked a good dinner. The people on the big rock ate it. Then they all went to the church. And that was the first Thanksgiving. It was a long story, and I got mixed up.

Peter said he saw an Indian on television shoot a man with a bow and arrow. A girl chased the Indian and locked him up in a house and burned the house down. That was a lot better story. Mrs. Turner had a hard time getting us to listen to her again.

We cut out turkeys today. "Stay on the lines," Miss Cora said. I could hardly do it around the turkey's little feet. Chucky made his turkey fight Hughy's turkey. Hughy cut off Chucky's turkey's head just like the farmer does. He did it with his scissors. Miss Cora made Hughy give Chucky *his* turkey. Chucky didn't want it. He threw it on the floor.

Hughy didn't run away today. But he told his mother the teacher took his turkey away from him. She said she'd stay in our room with him after this.

Daddy brought us home today, and Mommy stayed for church. Sometimes Mommy brings us home and Daddy stays. Mommy wishes there was a nursery so she and Daddy could both stay. Miss Cora told Mommy they tried it one time and there weren't enough mothers to help.

The church is looking for a new preacher. The old one wore out.

6 ⬜ PICTURES FOR BIG PEOPLE

I wish it was Thanksgiving every day. Grandmother Lowell made some special little pies for Janet and Keith and Lowell and me. I like to go to Grandmother's house.

Grandmother says I'm just like Mommy when she was a little girl—my eyes the same blue and my hair the same curls. But when I go to Grandma Quick's house, she says I'm just like Daddy was when he was a little boy.

We stayed more than one day. We stayed at night. And we went to Sunday school where my mother went when she was a little girl. Mommy thinks it's nicer now even than when Miss Ruth was the teacher. They have toys to play with. And a nice rug to sit on. And you don't sit at big tables. The teacher let me hold a picture 'cause I was visiting.

After Thanksgiving comes Christmas. You know what I want for Christmas? A puppy dog. Mommy had a dog when she was my size. His name was Mugs. Daddy says everybody who moves to Rose Park gets a dog. All but Mrs. Spencer on our street. She doesn't like dogs. And if we step on her yard, she yells at us.

When we walked through a big room at church this morning, it was dark. Mommy said there was to be a movie.

Hughy was crying when his mother brought him to our room. He wanted to see the movie. His mother asked why couldn't the kindergarten children see the movie. She didn't think it was fair for the big children to see it and for us not to.

So we saw it. But it went too fast. The people in it talked too fast, and they said funny words. They had on funny clothes too. The men wore bathrobes. Some bad soldiers on horses hit a man on the ground real hard—with a big whip. Another man said go find the baby. He wanted to kill the baby.

I was scared. But Mommy told me it was the Baby Jesus, and he didn't get dead. Mommy said it wasn't a little children's movie. I like Donald Duck better.

We went back to our room. Mrs. Turner told us Jesus is going to have a birthday. It's Christmas. But he doesn't come to our Sunday school. He's a baby.

Mrs. Turner put a picture on the wall. She called my name—"Kathy Ann, what do you see in the picture?" But I couldn't see very well. It was 'way up high where Mrs. Turner's eyes are. All I could see was a box.

She told us it's the manger where Baby Jesus stays. I don't know what is a manger.

Mrs. Turner showed us some pictures in a big book, too. There was a lady with wings talking to the sheeps. Then she flew away.

7 ⬚ A FUNNY STATION

I had to sit in the same chair with Maribel this morning. Daddy says everybody comes to Sunday school when it's Christmas. Maribel doesn't cry any more. But she doesn't smile.

People kept coming into our room. We stopped singing while Mrs. Turner talked to a man. You call him the Super-something. He's the boss of the Sunday school. Mrs. Turner kept saying, "All-right-all-right-all-right."

After he was gone, she had a lot of things to tell us—too many things. I can't remember them all.

Mr. Super-something wants us to come upstairs with all the big children and the grownups next Sunday. He wants us to sing and say speeches. A speech is to say by yourself.

Hughy's mother said he already knew a speech. Mrs. Turner told Joyce and me to stay after Sunday school and she would give us speeches.

She said Santa Claus was glad to see so many children at Sunday school. I wish he would bring us some new chairs for Christmas so I can have one my own size for my own self every Sunday.

Mrs. Turner can ask him. I'll ask him for a puppy dog. Mommy and Daddy and Lowell and I are all going to see Santa Claus at a big store in the city and eat dinner in the store, too. I tried to tell Mrs. Turner about it this morning, but she said let somebody else talk. I'm somebody.

She let a lady come in and talk. Only I don't know very well what she talked about. Her words were too big. She said send Christmas presents to a "station." It's a funny station—not the same station where Daddy catches the train every morning. People live at this station. And their skin isn't white like mine. Their skin is yellow. I guess they're funny people.

They're poor, too, like the Thanksgiving people. We have to give them food and clothes. "Wrap-in-white-and-bring-next-Sunday."

Then Mr. Super-something came back in. He forgot to tell us to come to a party next Saturday, every single body in the whole Sunday school.

When Sunday school was over, Mrs. Turner looked in a

book and found a speech for me and one for Joyce. She wrote them on paper for us.

Mommy has been teaching mine to me tonight. I can say this much of it now:

> In Bethel-hem once long ago
> The angel voices rang.

I found out what is an angel. It's the lady with wings Mrs. Turner showed us a picture of. I never saw an angel. Mommy never saw an angel. I wonder where are the angels.

I found out about the station where the yellow people live. Mommy couldn't guess. But Daddy did. You know what, it's a "mission station." That's a place where somebody tells the people about Baby Jesus. The somebody is called a "missionary." Why didn't the lady at church tell those things the way Daddy does?

We have Christmas bells in our living-room windows and Christmas candles over our fireplace. They make me feel like Christmas. There weren't any Christmas things in our room at Sunday school. It isn't like a home.

8 GRAB BAG

There were lots and lots of children at the big store to see Santa Claus! I let Lowell go first. But he got scared and wouldn't talk. I helped him. I told Santa Claus we both want a puppy dog. Santa Claus had a fat tummy.

We ate dinner in a big room with a real tall Christmas tree. And I drank chocolate milk through a straw. A lady at another table asked to take me home with her. That's one of the funny things big people always say. I'm not going home with any of them.

Last night we went to the party at church. It was for the mothers and daddies and babies and everybody. Not many daddies were there. My daddy didn't like it very well. Lowell and I played games, but Mommy and Daddy mostly just sat.

We took presents for the grab bag. I took a storybook about Mrs. Goose, and Lowell took an elephant that moves. We like what we took better than what we got. I grabbed a little dish to keep pins in. But I haven't any pins to keep. Lowell grabbed a little car with just three wheels. One was gone.

Lowell kept saying, "Daddy fix it! Daddy fix it!"

Mr. Super-something stood up in front and talked. I found out his name. It's Mr. Broshaw. He's been boss of the Sunday school a long, long time. He said somebody thought we shouldn't have a party this year, but he told them we must have one 'cause there's *always* been a Christmas party. Santa Claus would feel bad if we didn't have one, 'cause he *always* comes to our party.

Santa Claus came, but I think he must have been feeling bad already. He wasn't big and fat like he was when we saw him in the store downtown.

Mr. Broshaw told Santa Claus we had been good boys and girls all year. So Santa Claus gave each one of us a little red sock with hard-to-chew candy in it. I like soft candy. We had ice cream, too. It was too soft. Lowell dripped all over his front.

After we got home, Lowell wouldn't go to sleep till his little car was fixed. Daddy looked and looked for something to make a wheel. Mommy said why not use a big button. It worked. Daddy would like to find who put that car in the grab bag.

Lowell was sleepy this morning when Daddy called us. The party made him stay up too late last night. But I was wide-awake, 'cause I was going to say a speech at Sunday school. Mommy remembered this time about the white

24

presents to take for the yellow people at the mission station.

Ellen took an old dress of hers that she didn't like and wouldn't wear any more. But I took my best coat from last year that isn't big enough since I've grown. Mommy says we should give nice things we like. I liked that coat. Lowell took pretty soap.

There was a Christmas tree upstairs at church, and under it was Baby Jesus in his box bed. We went up and stood by the tree and sang "Jesus Loves Me" and "Praise Him." Lowell saw Mommy and Daddy, and he waved "Hi!" at them. People laughed and said, "Isn't he cute!" So he waved some more.

I stepped out in front and said my speech, "In Bethel-hem once long ago." I talked loud just like Daddy told me, and I didn't do anything wrong. The people clapped their hands real hard.

Then Hughy did his speech. But he forgot and his mother had to help him. Joyce talked so soft nobody could hear her. I said mine the best of anybody!

I got tired of other children's speeches and songs. Joyce and I turned around in our seat to look at people. Some lady shook her head at us.

Mr. Broshaw told us to carry our white presents to Baby Jesus. So we laid them by the box bed. But I thought they were for the yellow people. Baby Jesus would look funny in my last year's coat.

9 VANILLA AND DISHRAGS

We *did* get a puppy for Christmas. He's a tan and white cocker, and he's the cutest dog in Rose Park. Daddy says he bosses the house like a judge in court. So we call him "Your Honor." Mostly we say "Y'honor." He has his own little bed, but he likes getting in bed with Lowell or me better, or up in Daddy's chair.

Daddy wouldn't let me take Y'honor to Sunday school today. Chucky rode his new two-wheeler. Is it ever nice! I wish I had one. Hughy brought his little tractor, and Joyce brought her Christmas doll. Mrs. Turner put the toys on the piano, 'cause you don't play with things at Sunday school. You go there to learn. That's what Mrs. Turner said.

You know what, Mrs. Turner won't be our teacher any more. She has too much to do. George didn't want her to be our teacher. He wants her to stay home and eat breakfast with him. That's what she told Miss Cora.

The first thing we did today was to go upstairs. Mr. Broshaw talked. He liked having the whole Sunday school together the way we were for Christmas. That's the way it was when he was a boy. Only we won't go upstairs every Sunday—just the first-Sunday-in-the-month.

He's going to give us prizes like at a birthday party when you drop the clothespins into the milk bottle. If we don't miss Sunday school a single time, we'll get a pin to wear. When he was a boy, he got a whole bunch of pins.

Upstairs they didn't sing any songs I knew. They sang out of books. Joyce and I held a book and made noises. But I'd rather sing real words. There was a song about a lamb. He got blood all over. Somebody hurt the poor little lamb.

A lady went up front. She said everybody buy vanilla and dishrags from her so she can build a new church. She's the one who stepped on Lowell's money. He dropped it and I had to find it for him. It rolled and rolled.

We made a big noise when we went downstairs. Peter hid under the table. Chucky put his chair on top of the table and sat in it. Mrs. Turner didn't know Peter was under

26

the table. When she called his name, he didn't say, "Here." We laughed, and Hughy said, "Peter's under the table."

Mrs. Turner made him come out. She said going upstairs makes us excited. She feels very bad if we aren't good children on her last Sunday.

She told us a hundred things. Mrs. Turner wants you to be good for your new teacher. Mrs. Turner wants you to bring your pennies every Sunday. Mrs. Turner wants you to show the new teacher how nice you can draw and color. Mrs. Turner wants you to say your verses real nice for the new teacher. Mrs. Turner wants you to sing loud for the new teacher.

I wonder why she talks to herself. "Mrs. Turner" is for other people to call her.

Miss Cora told us to say good-by to Mrs. Turner. So we all said it together real loud—"GOOD-BY-MRS.-TURNER!" I said it the loudest of anybody.

10 A SUNBEAN FOR JESUS

Mrs. Wright is our new teacher. Her hair isn't curls. She has a black dress. She just moved to Rose Park. She used to be the kindergarten teacher in another church. She doesn't have any little girls and boys of her own. They're grown up now.

The kindergarten room she used to have was bigger than ours. She is going to change ours.

So we did something different today. Mrs. Wright and Miss Cora pushed the tables 'way back. Then they put all the chairs together. Mrs. Wright stood up in front of us. Miss Cora sat by the piano.

We're to sit on the chairs every Sunday when we get there. I sat by a new girl today. Her name is Gail. I liked her. Her mother was there too. She is a smiley mother. She had on a dress with flowers in it. She asked me to help Gail sing. When Joyce came, I told her I had somebody else to sit by instead of her.

When Sunday school was ready to start, Mrs. Wright said some words. They're about the Lord's house. And you know what? The Lord's house is the church! Isn't that a funny thing to call the church? Another funny word is "silence." It means be quiet.

Be-quiet-at-church—that's what Mrs. Wright told us, only she used the funny words. She said she'll do these things every single Sunday.

After she says be quiet, then we sing good and loud.

Mrs. Wright knows a new song! About sunbeans. She said, "Let's learn it. It goes this way." She sang, "Jesus wants me—," then we sang, "Jesus wants me." She sang, "for a sunbean—," and we sang, "for a sunbean." There were lots more parts. I don't remember them now.

Something else new. Mrs. Wright asked me and Chucky to pass the basket. He stood on one side and I stood on the other. Peter had to set the basket on the floor while he looked for his pennies. He looked in all his pockets, and he didn't have any. His daddy forgot.

Ellen wasn't ready for the basket either. Her money was tied up in her hanky. Gail's mother got it out for her. Patsy is so little she didn't want to put her money in. She wanted to take some out.

Just then Waldo came in. We waited for him to get his pennies out of his glove. Mrs. Wright told us to hurry up and not take such a long time.

Mrs. Wright held up a black book and asked us what it was. I knew. It's the Bible. Mrs. Wright said she will read us a Bible story every Sunday.

Jesus was a baby on Christmas. But today he was a man. He went fishing with his friends. His friends didn't catch any fish till Jesus came. Jesus knew how to catch fish. He made them catch a whole boat full. That's more than Chucky's daddy catches.

Jesus wants all of us to go fishing and bring children to Sunday school. Mrs. Wright likes lots of boys and girls at Sunday school, even as little as Lowell and Patsy, who aren't old enough for our room.

When Mommy came after me, I asked her couldn't Gail go home with me. Mommy talked to Gail's mother.

Gail did come to see me after dinner, and we played. We didn't play with Joyce. Mommy likes Gail's mother. Her name is Mrs. Gordon.

11 RED STAR, BLUE STAR

There were so many at Sunday school today that I had to sit on a box with Hughy. He sneezed all the time. And he didn't put his hand over his mouth. His mother kept saying, "Hughy-use-your-hanky." She wants him to win the prize pin. Mommy says maybe I'll sneeze too.

We learned the B-I-B-L-E song. You stand on the B-I-B-L-E. I like to say it—B-I-B-L-E. I wonder what it means.

We did something else different today. After we'd sat together on our chairs—only I sat on a box—we went to the tables. We're going to have classes the way they did at Mrs. Wright's other church. We had to wait while she and Miss Cora pulled the tables out. Then we had to carry the chairs to the tables, and our coats fell off the chairs.

Mrs. Wright called our names and told us what table to sit at. You know what, Gail's mother is the teacher for one table! I wanted to be in her class, but I'm not. Gail and I are in Mrs. Wright's class. Miss Cora teaches the other table.

Each Sunday we're at Sunday school Mrs. Wright will paste a red star by our names in her little book.

She gave us papers to take home. They're not like the ones we used to get. Mrs. Wright said she likes these better, 'cause every single one has a Bible story in it.

Today's story was about Ruth. I said, "Miss Ruth is a friend of my mother's!" Mrs. Wright told me not to talk when she was reading the story. She said it wasn't the same Ruth.

Ruth went out in the field to look for something to eat, 'cause she was hungry. A nice farmer gave her food, and she went home and cooked her own bread. And she wasn't hungry any more.

Mrs. Wright said there are lots of boys and girls far away from here who are hungry. They aren't lucky like we are. So we should say thank you to God for giving us our good dinner. The other children don't have a good dinner. I wonder why God doesn't give them a good dinner.

We colored pictures on our little papers—a glass of milk and a banana and oatmeal. Stay in the lines, no scribbly pictures, Mrs. Wright told us. Show them to our mothers and daddies and ask them to read us the story again. 'Cause next Sunday she'll ask us if we remember what the story was about. If we remember, she'll give us a *blue* star.

Gail and Joyce and Chucky all came to my house after dinner. We played Sunday school. Mommy let us put all the chairs together. Joyce's mother won't let us play in the living room. She's always cleaning the house.

When we played Sunday school, I was Mrs. Wright. I told the others what to do. Be quiet in the Lord's house and I'll read you the lesson. Stay in the lines. Stand on the B-I-B-L-E.

Daddy heard us, and he told me what that means. It's the Bible! But you shouldn't stand on the Bible. That's not a nice way to treat books. Daddy says it doesn't mean to stand with your feet. I asked him what other way can you stand, but he wouldn't tell me. He just said it was too hard a song for little children to understand.

12 MRS. WRIGHT'S SHOW

I *did* sneeze like Hughy. Mommy is mad at Hughy. I had to stay in the house for two days. But I had fun with Y'honor. Mommy got mad at him too. He chewed up one of her stockings.

Lowell and Chucky and I had fun making a snow fort yesterday. But Mrs. Wright doesn't like snow and so many boots and wraps at Sunday school.

Today she brought a box for us to put our boots in. Mr. Mac, the man who takes care of the church, brought in a thing somebody found to put hangers on for our coats. It's up high, so the teachers have to hang them for us. Mrs. Wright made us keep leggings on, 'cause they're so much trouble. I don't like leggings on in the house. They're *going* clothes.

Mrs. Wright showed us something that looked like a little blackboard. But it wasn't. It's a flannelboard. She said she has *always* liked a flannelboard. She can do lots of things with it. Today she did a story with it. The story about Baby

31

Moses. She told us to watch everything she did. She used both hands, and she talked at the same time.

She put paper dolls on the board, and they stuck. First she put paper-doll-bad-king on the board. Then she put the soldiers in front of the king. The king said go kill all the boy babies.

Baby Moses was a cute little paper doll. His mother—and his father—and his big sister—all got stuck on the flannelboard. They put Baby Moses in a basket. His mother set him on the water like a little boat. His sister hid in the weeds.

Then Mrs. Wright made the prettiest paper doll walk on. That was the princess. Some other girls were with her. One of them took Baby Moses out of the basket. She gave him to the princess, only the princess couldn't hold him, 'cause Mrs. Wright tore the paper. Mrs. Wright tried hard to catch him, but he fell off the flannelboard. We laughed. Mrs. Wright didn't laugh. She said Moses wasn't supposed to fall off.

The princess didn't want her father, the bad old king, to kill this baby. Moses' sister said she'd get a nurse for the baby. Mrs. Wright ran her off the flannelboard, and guess who came back to be nurse—Baby Moses' mother!

Then Mrs. Wright said she would tell the story again, and we could put the paper dolls on and off the flannelboard if we'd be very careful.

We all wanted to help. Mrs. Wright said stay in our seats till she called our names. Then she'd hand us the paper dolls to stick on.

Peter got to put on the bad king. All of us held up our hands to stick on Baby Moses. Mrs. Wright let Waldo do it. But Waldo put Baby Moses on top of the weeds. Mrs. Wright said, "No, no, Waldo! On the water." And she moved him to the right place.

Mrs. Wright didn't like the way I let Baby Moses' sister

take little short, slow steps—so I could stand up there longer.
She said, "Hurry up, Kathy Ann."

When the paper dolls were all used up, Hughy yelled that
he didn't ever put any bodies on. Mrs. Wright let him stick
a soldier on. "Here I come to kill the babies!" he said.

Lowell and Patsy wanted to touch all the dolls. Mrs.
Wright made them go back to their chairs. They're too
little.

At our table Mrs. Wright let us whisper in her ear if we
remembered what the story was about last Sunday. Gail and
I were the only ones who knew. So we got the blue stars.
I remembered 'cause Mommy told me as we left home this
morning. It was about—oh, my, I've forgot. But I don't care
—I already have my blue star.

I had trouble getting my boots un-mixed-up when we
were ready to go home.

13 I CAN'T SEE HIM

God was at our Sunday school today. I didn't see
him, but he was there. Mrs. Wright said so. I think he came
in when I had my eyes shut.

This was the day to go upstairs. There weren't enough
places for everybody to sit down. Daddy and some other
men stood up. Everybody wants to win the prize pin.

One man talked about a new church. His name was Mr.
Block. Chucky said, "Knock his block off!" and we laughed.

When we went downstairs, Mrs. Wright didn't have
time for classes. We sat in the chairs. The mothers sat on
the tables.

Mrs. Wright had another surprise—a box with purple
all over it. She put some candles on top and lighted them.
She laid her black Bible down on it too. I don't know why.

Hughy and Maribel passed the basket today. When Patsy tried to give the basket to Maribel, it fell down. The pennies rolled on the floor. Maribel's mother said, "You should have been more careful, Maribel!"

But Gail's mother was nice. She helped Maribel pick up the money. Then Maribel and Hughy took the basket up to Mrs. Wright. She told us all to say, "The-Lord-loveth-a-cheerful-giver." It means God wants us to bring pennies. Mrs. Wright set the basket on the purple box.

We sang our songs, and Miss Cora asked Mrs. Wright should she call the roll next or would we say prayers. Mrs. Wright wanted prayers. She showed us how to do it. Bow your head. Shut your eyes. Fold your hands. Lowell put his hands clear over his face. Now you're ready to talk to God. Only I didn't feel ready. I didn't know what to tell him.

But I didn't have to talk. Mrs. Wright talked. She told

34

God it was a pretty day and we were at Sunday school and for him to help us learn our lesson and be good.

Mrs. Wright said God heard everything she told him. He can hear us, too. We can bow our heads, shut our eyes, fold our hands, and talk to God any time we want. He'll hear 'cause he's everywhere. He's at my house and Joyce's house and Chucky's house and up in the trees and in the piano and in Mommy's typewriter and in Daddy's brief case.

I wish Daddy was God. Then he could be at the office and at home at the same time. I guess God is like Superman. He can fly all around without anybody seeing him.

Today Chucky and I were playing in the yard. Chucky had his gun and he was shooting up in the air, Bang! Bang! I yelled at him not to do that 'cause he might shoot God.

Mrs. Wright told us to talk to God before we go to bed. Tonight I'm going to shut my eyes and bow my head and fold my hands and say, "Dear God, I wish you'd let me see what you look like."

14 ⌑ GOD AND THE BAD PEOPLE

I have a new snow suit. Mommy and Mrs. Gordon went to the city yesterday. Gail stayed at my house, and we helped Daddy paint the basement. When it's finished, it will be our playroom. It's all pretty yellow and green.

I wore my new snow suit to Sunday school this morning. Everybody said it looked nice. It's the prettiest snow suit of anybody's in the whole room. Miss Cora hung it up for me. I told her Mommy got it on sale so it didn't cost as much now as if I'd got it before Christmas.

Mrs. Wright showed a new story on the flannelboard. She made it sound kind of scary. It was about Noah. God liked Noah 'cause he was good. But God didn't like the bad people. He made it rain and rain and rain till there was a big flood and all the bad people got dead. Noah built a giant boat called an ark, and when it rained, he took the animals in the boat with him, and they didn't get dead.

Then Mrs. Wright told us if we'd be careful and do it the way she did, we could put the paper dolls on the board. She let me be one of the giraffes. Waldo put the rainbow on upside down. Mrs. Wright said, "Oh, no, not that way," and fixed it right. Waldo went back to his seat and kicked Chucky's leg, and Chucky hit Waldo on the arm, and Mrs. Wright spoke cross to them—"Boys, you must behave in Sunday school."

Mrs. Wright said God sent the rainbow to tell Noah he'd never make another flood. But Peter said there was another flood—where his grandma lives—and the water came right into her house, and she had to climb up on the roof. Mrs. Wright said that was too bad.

She talked some more about God. (I think Sunday-school teachers talk too much.) God can do anything. He made the trees and the flowers and the birds and the sun and the moon and the stars. He's the boss of the whole world. I guess he must work all the time. But I still haven't seen him. And why did he sent the flood on Peter's grandma?

Today while Mrs. Wright was talking to God, I peeked. I didn't see him, but I saw the funniest bug with long legs. It climbed up and up and up the wall clear to the ceiling. I watched it all the way up.

Mrs. Wright said we were good to listen so nice and quiet while she was praying. I wonder where that bug went.

The Sunday-school wall isn't pretty and yellow the way our basement is that Daddy is painting. It isn't any color at all. The tables aren't pretty and shiny either.

At our table we made paper chains, 'cause Mrs. Wright told us to. At Mrs. Gordon's table they cut out pictures from magazines and pasted them on colored paper. I'd rather do that. I wanted to go over to her table. Mrs. Wright asked her why weren't they making chains like the teacher's book said.

This afternoon Chucky and Joyce and Gail and Lowell and I played Noah's ark. I was God. I poured water on the bad people till they got dead.

I like to play I'm somebody else. The other day Mommy called me to come in the house. I had to finish something first. Mommy called again. She said, "Y'honor, just a little puppy dog, minds better than you. He comes when he's called."

I laughed. I got down on my hands like I was a doggie. I said, "Whistle to me, Mommy!"

Mommy whistled. It was fun. I ran in real fast.

15 PINK DONKEY

Mrs. Wright told us today we're big enough to say prayers by ourselves at Sunday school. We all bowed our heads and folded our hands and shut our eyes. Nobody said anything.

Mrs. Wright called my name. "Kathy Ann, can't you say a prayer for me?"

I thought prayers were for God. But anyway I couldn't think of any. She asked me too fast.

Miss Cora whispered to me, "Say 'help-me-to-be-a-good-girl.'"

So that's what I said—"Say help me to be a good girl."

Mrs. Wright told me, "That was a fine prayer, Kathy Ann." I guess I'm the smartest one in the kindergarten.

After we opened our eyes, Mrs. Wright told us to look around and see what we should thank God for. We named

a lot of things. The piano—and the piano stool—the tables
—and our shoes—and the flannelboard—and the windows
—gloves—and coats—and buttons on the coats—and
snow suits—and boots. It was like a game. Gail and Ellen
and I tried to see who could think of the most things.

At our table Mrs. Wright read about the Good Somebody who helped a sick man on the road. Two men walked
by—step, step, step—and didn't help the poor man at all.
But when the Good Somebody came by on his donkey—
trot, trot, trot—he stopped. He put the sick man on his
donkey and gave him medicine and took him to a motel.

Jesus wants us to be kind like that man. Mrs. Wright
said, "Let's have a little prayer." And this time she started,
"Dear Jesus." I get Jesus and God mixed up!

Mrs. Wright asked us, "Suppose you hit and pushed your
friends, would that be kind?"

We said NO! Peter told that a boy where he used to live
hit him and made his nose bleed one time. And I told how
Joyce pushed Lowell down the other day when he took her
doll. We all knew some bad children.

On the back of our story paper was a picture of the
donkey the Good Somebody rode. Mrs. Wright showed us
how to make other donkeys just like it on colored paper. I
made a pink donkey. We chased each other's donkeys,
trot, trot, trot.

Just before time to get our wraps un-mixed-up, Mrs.
Wright had us to say our Bible verse all together: "Be-ye-
kind-one-to-another." I said it real loud.

When we were ready to go home, I couldn't find my
pink donkey. Peter had a pink donkey. I said give it to me.
He said it was his. He pushed me. I hit him.

Miss Cora stopped us. She said, "Remember the nice
verse about be-ye-kind." But Peter wasn't kind.

Joyce found my pink donkey on the floor.

16 MRS. WRIGHT IS WRONG

Mommy said I got up on the wrong side of the bed. But it's the same side I always get out of. I can't get out of the other side, 'cause it's next to the wall. And I can't crawl over the end, 'cause Y'honor lies there.

Anyway I didn't feel like a good day. At breakfast Mommy put some white stuff in my dish. I asked her, "What's that?" and she said, "Mush."

I told her, "I don't like it. I don't want it."

And she took my mush and dumped it into her dish.

That made me cry—"You took my mush!"

Mommy said I said I didn't want it.

But, I told her, I was going to change my mind! She didn't give me time.

Daddy choked on his mush.

I didn't feel much like Sunday school. Not even for a red star and a blue star and a prize pin. But Daddy promised if we went to Sunday school, he'd take us to see Grandma and Grandpa Quick after dinner.

We learned a new word today—"altar." That's the box with the purple cloth and the candles and the Bible and Mrs. Wright's pocketbook. She let Ellen light the candles today. Jesus wants us to be little candles shining in the dark. I'd rather be a child.

Jesus-and-God want so many things. I get tired of them sometimes.

And now I have to learn a long prayer that Jesus used to say. The one the big people at church say when they bow their heads and shut their eyes and go mum-mum-mum.

Mrs. Wright stood by the altar and had us say it after her. That's when Waldo came in. He didn't want to say it. It starts out, "Our Father." My daddy is a father.

39

Jesus . . . God . . . Lord . . . Father. Every Sunday Mrs. Wright says something different.

She gave us each one a paper with the prayer on it—to take home and mem-o-rize. The children in her other kindergarten all learned the Lord's Prayer before they went into first grade. I wonder why can't you learn it when you're big enough to know the hard words. But Mrs. Wright says learn it to say upstairs. She'll give us a gold star.

When we were going to our table, I dropped my paper with the Lord's Prayer on it. Hughy stepped on it and wouldn't move his feet. I stepped on his foot hard. He cried. His mother said, "What did you do to him?"

Mrs. Wright took me behind the piano and said, "Kathy Ann, God doesn't like you acting this way today."

I was afraid. I don't like for God to be mad at me. I don't want him to make me get dead.

Grandma Quick asked me did I feel all right.

I feel all right now. I asked Mommy if God was mad at me for being bad today. And she said no. God is just like your mother and father—he loves you even when you're

40

bad. That's why you call him "Father" sometimes. Miss Ruth told Mommy about it when Mommy was a little girl.

I'm glad I have a mother and father to tell me things right if Mrs. Wright tells me wrong.

17 JUST A BULB

We went upstairs today. Mrs. Wright told us there would be a surprise. It was a man. His name is Dr. Hart. He isn't a people-doctor who gives you medicine. He's a preacher-doctor. A preacher stands up and talks at church.

Dr. Hart is our new preacher. And you know what, he has a little girl named Judy just the same size as me. I like Dr. Hart. He talks up and down instead of mum-mum-mum. And he laughs.

There's a Mrs. Hart too. She has a smiley face.

When we went back downstairs, Dr. Hart stood at the door and shook hands with all of us. Judy came down to our room. Mrs. Wright asked her too many things did she want to do. Judy shook her head and swang her feet. She's new.

Easter is coming. After Easter I'll be five years old! I remember Easter. That's when you get candy eggs in baskets. You have pretty flowers at Easter too. Mrs. Wright told us to go home and ask our mothers for a bulb to put in the dirt. It will grow into a beautiful flower for Easter.

You talk about Jesus at Easter too. Every Sunday we'll have a story about Jesus. Story, story, story! Today Jesus was out in a boat with his friends. He went to sleep, and there was a big storm. Wind and rain and water came into the boat. The friends were scared.

One of them waked Jesus up. Jesus put his hand out and

41

said go away, storm, and it did—like magic. I wish I could do that.

Today Mommy and Daddy both wanted to stay for church to hear Dr. Hart preach. Mommy asked Lowell and me would we stay. Maribel's mother said Maribel stays— she lets her draw pictures but not eat crackers—and she pounds it into Maribel's head that she's going to stay.

Lowell and I promised to try to be quiet. We sat behind a woman with a funny hat. There was a long feather on it. Lowell liked to touch the feather. I turned all the pages in the songbook, and the feather woman looked around to see what I was doing.

Daddy gave each one of us a pencil and paper. I drew big pictures and used the paper up fast. Lowell dropped his pencil. The feather woman didn't like picking it up.

Daddy says give us to Maribel's mother. But Mommy thinks there should be a special place for us to stay during church.

After we got home, I remembered about the bulb. I went to the basement and got one. I put it in a can and started outdoors. Mommy asked where was I going. I told her to get dirt to put on the bulb so I'd have a beautiful flower for Easter.

She said, oh, no, that wasn't the right kind of bulb. You can't use a lamp bulb. You have to have a flower bulb! But Mrs. Wright just said "bulb."

18 | I DON'T SEE HOW . . .

My mother was one of the teachers in my Sunday school today. Miss Cora was climbing up on a chair to clean her cupboard and she fell and hurt her ankle. So she couldn't come to Sunday school. Mommy and I took a lemon pie to her.

Mrs. Wright asked Mommy to teach Miss Cora's class. She came to our house last night and gave Mommy a book. Mommy told her she didn't know how to teach a Sunday-school class. Mommy was never any kind of teacher.

But Mrs. Wright said anybody can teach *little* children —just keep them quiet and do what the book says. Mommy read the book last night and some more this morning while we ate breakfast. Daddy joked her that he'd give her a book to read and she could help him with his next case.

Mommy didn't like the Sunday-school book very well. I wanted to sit at her table this morning, but she said no, I had to stay with Mrs. Wright. I'd like to move around at Sunday school.

Mrs. Wright brought an Easter lily. It was beau-ti-ful. I wanted to smell it and touch it, but she put it on top of the piano. She was afraid we'd hurt it. I wouldn't hurt it.

Chucky and Ellen got gold stars for saying the Lord's Prayer. I didn't. I learned the "leadus" part, but now I forgot the "Our Father" part. But I have more red and blue stars than anybody.

Judy Hart's mother visited our kindergarten today. Mrs. Wright said let's show her all the things we know and not make any mistakes. We sang "Jesus Wants Me for a Sunbean," and we told about Baby Moses. Then we said memory verses. I was afraid I'd make a mistake.

We learned an Easter song. It's about Jesus going shopping. "He paid the price, he paid the price."

Mrs. Wright told us a sad story. Some bad people killed Jesus. They shouldn't have done it. God should have stopped them. Jesus was friends with everybody. I don't like it for the bad people to be mean to him.

But he didn't stay dead. He came right out of the ground

and got alive again. His friends saw him, and he looked like he always did, with the long white dress on.

It was Easter when he got alive again. Then God took him up in the sky to live with him. That's where heaven is. But they don't stay there all the time, 'cause they're right here with us too. I don't see how they do it.

We had the Easter story today 'cause there won't be any Sunday school on Easter. So many people will come to church that Dr. Hart will preach two times. There isn't room for them and us children both, and anyway, if we made noise downstairs, they'd hear us upstairs.

When we were ready to go home, Mr. Broshaw came to the door. He gave each one of us a present. A green thing. We didn't know what it was for.

Mommy and Daddy got one too. They call it a "palm." You wave it at Jesus.

Mommy and I went over to Gail's house after dinner. Mommy and Mrs. Gordon talked about Sunday school. Mrs. Gordon doesn't like the Sunday-school book either. She used to be a teacher in everyday school. And one time she helped a kindergarten teacher in another church.

TEACH THE TEACHERS!

19 ## FUNNY?

I'm five years old! I had a birthday party, and Daddy played games with us. Mommy made an angel-food cake like a little merry-go-round. It had blue icing. I like blue. Mommy never saw a cake with blue icing, but if I wanted blue, I could have it.

Mommy and Daddy gave me a doll house. Maybe when I'm six years old, I can have a two-wheeler.

While we were having my party, Y'honor ran and barked at us. He had fun too. But when we weren't watching, he ran across the street to Mrs. Spencer's house. Mrs. Spencer was digging in her garden. Y'honor ran where she was and she fell down.

Daddy and I went over real fast, and Mrs. Spencer said Y'honor knocked her down. I picked up Y'honor and patted him and asked him, "Are you hurt, Y'honor?"

The party children came over, and they all said, "Is Y'honor hurt?"

Mrs. Spencer got mad. She said keep that dog at home or she'd call the police. Daddy told her he was sorry. I'm not. Mrs. Spencer doesn't like doggies and children.

Today Mrs. Wright burned the candles on the Sunday-school cake for me, and I blew them all out at one time. I'm a strong blower. I put my pennies in the kitty-cat bank. Mrs. Wright said the birthday wish for me, about sunshine and birthdays in heaven. But I don't want to go 'way up in the sky. I want to stay here with Mommy and Daddy.

Dr. Hart came in to visit us, and we said the Lord's Prayer for him. Then I said it by myself, and now I have my gold star. I still don't know what the words mean, but I can say them.

Dr. Hart invited us to come visit him in his office sometime. He hopes that someday we'll have a new church with lots of room for kindergartners. He asked Mrs. Wright and Mrs. Gordon and Miss Cora to come to a meeting.

Children's Day is coming. That's when we go upstairs and show our mothers and daddies all the things we've learned. That's when we'll get our prize pins.

This afternoon Mrs. Gordon came over to see Mommy. Mommy told me to run play, but I didn't run very far. I heard what Mrs. Gordon said. Mrs. Wright is mad. At the teachers' meeting today Dr. Hart asked all the teachers to come to a "training school."

Mrs. Wright doesn't want to go to the training school—she never learns anything when she goes.

Mrs. Gordon is going. Some people are coming out from the city to teach the teachers. Isn't that funny?

Mrs. Gordon wants Mommy to go to the training school. Mommy will think about it.

20 I'M A HOLLYHOCK

Mrs. Wright isn't our teacher any more! I heard Mommy tell Daddy about it. Mrs. Wright told Mr. Broshaw that if Dr. Hart didn't like the way she taught Sunday school, he could find somebody else. She's tried other ways, but she likes her way better.

Dr. Hart asked Mrs. Gordon to be teacher for the whole kindergarten. She can't do it this summer, 'cause they're going on a trip, but she'll do it in September. I'm glad! I like her and she likes me.

And you know what, my mother will help her! Dr. Hart came to see Mommy and talked a long time. He gave her a book to read, and she's going with Mrs. Gordon to the training school to learn about kindergarten children like me. Daddy says he knows too much already.

Dr. Hart found us a teacher for the summer. Her name is Miss Gay. When Dr. Hart was visiting people's houses, he found her. She just loves children. She wears a hat all the time at Sunday school like she's going instead of staying.

When I got there this morning, she grabbed me. "Hello, darling! You're just the little girl Miss Gay was looking for. You'll be a hollyhock for Miss Gay, won't you, sweetheart?"

I didn't know what she was talking about. She pinned a piece of paper on me. I feel funny for people I don't know to call me darling sweetheart. And I don't like being talked to like a baby when I'm five years old!

When she saw Lowell, she said, "What a sweet little boy! Miss Gay can use him for a rosebud."

Everybody who came to the room, she said, "Darling, Miss Gay wants you for her flower garden!" Gail is a daisy and Joyce is a morning glory. Chucky is a butterfly.

It's for Children's Day. I thought we were to show our mothers and daddies things we already knew. But now we have to learn to be flowers just for Children's Day.

Miss Gay reads about an old lady named Mother Nature who goes for a walk. When she comes to me and Peter sitting down, she says, "Who are you?"

We stand up real slow and say, "We're hollyhocks, Mother Nature, so tall and straight."

Mother Nature—really Miss Gay—asks all the children who they are. Lowell and Patsy wouldn't tell, so Miss Gay had to say it herself, "Little pink rosebuds."

Chucky pretends he's a butterfly and touches all the flowers. Then we all take hands and go round and round singing, "Oh, we're the summer flowers, blooming in the sun."

We didn't have time to learn the whole song, so Miss Gay wants us to come to the church to practice next Saturday. And we're to wear costumes.

Just as we were ready to go home, Miss Cora yelled,

"Wait, children, I forgot to call the roll!" She had a hard time.

Daddy came to get Lowell and me, and Miss Gay told him I was to wear red and Lowell was to wear pink for Children's Day. Daddy said she'd better call Mommy.

After dinner Miss Gay did call Mommy. She asked her would she make me a hollyhock costume out of crepe paper and show Peter's mother. Mommy has been looking up pictures of hollyhocks. She wishes I was something easy like sunflower—that's what Waldo is. I don't know why I'm anything.

21 PIN TROUBLE

Lowell wouldn't be a rosebud for Children's Day. Yesterday when we practiced, he would. But that was with his overalls on. When Mommy tried to put on his pink paper costume this morning, he said no, he didn't want to wear it.

Maribel's mother said she'd make him be a rosebud. But Mommy told him he could go sit with Daddy, and he did. Patsy was a rosebud by herself.

We had fun yesterday when we practiced in the big room upstairs. We chased one another up and down, and we walked on the seats. Hughy's mother kept saying, "You mustn't make noise in church."

But Miss Gay told us to talk real loud. She went to the back of the church, and when Peter and I said, "We're hollyhocks, Mother Nature, so tall and straight," she couldn't hear us. She said our mothers and fathers would feel so sad if they couldn't hear their little flowers.

This morning Miss Gay and Miss Cora and the mothers worked real fast to help us put our costumes on. Then we went upstairs. I knew what people would say—"Aren't they cute!" The daisies were the cutest. I wish I'd been a daisy.

Peter had trouble with his costume. The top part of his hollyhock slipped down over his face.

Miss Gay had a paper costume on too. She went up on the high place with us. Joyce made a mistake and went with the daisies instead of the morning glories.

You could hardly hear the zinnias. Miss Cora kept whispering, "Louder," so when it was our turn, we said real loud, "We're hollyhocks, Mother Nature, so tall and straight."

Chucky was looking at the people and didn't be a butterfly at the right time. Miss Gay had to say, "Butterfly, butterfly!" And there wasn't any sunflower—Waldo didn't get there at all.

When we went back to our seats, the people clapped their hands. Then the big boys and girls sang and said things. I got tired, and the crepe paper stuck my neck.

Mr. Broshaw read the names of the ones who didn't miss a Sunday. He read my name. We went up and he gave us a pin to wear. It isn't so very much of a prize, not like candy or balloons.

Joyce didn't get any. And Hughy didn't get any.

Hughy's mother was sitting next to Daddy. And she was mad. She said Hughy hadn't missed a Sunday. It wasn't fair. She'll take him to another Sunday school.

After we went back to our room, Hughy's mother came down—and *she* made noise in church. She talked loud to Miss Cora. Miss Cora looked in her little book. She found a mistake. Last Sunday Hughy was there, but he ran out before Miss Cora called his name.

Miss Cora said she was sorry. They gave Hughy a pin. But Hughy's mother still didn't have a smiley look.

[22] SAMUEL AND JESUS

You know what, Miss Ruth—Mommy's Sunday-school teacher when she was just my size—came to our house and stayed three days. Every day she went walking with Lowell and me. She played with Y'honor, and Y'honor liked her.

She's pretty old—older than Mommy. But she still teaches in Sunday school, and other days she teaches everyday school. She wears pretty dresses, and she has a smiley face.

Daddy says ladies like Miss Ruth ought to get hundreds of gold stars. They don't have any little boys and girls of their own, but they teach other people's boys and girls.

Mommy wasn't always good when she was little. Miss Ruth said she was pretty good, though. She's glad I'm writing a book just like Mommy did.

She's glad Mommy will be a Sunday-school teacher. Mommy told her she wanted Lowell and me to be happy at Sunday school the way she was when she was in Miss Ruth's class. She's always liked church 'cause Miss Ruth was her teacher.

Miss Ruth thinks Mommy should go to a "lab school." That's where you have Sunday school every day. And you know what, Mommy decided to go! She'll be away from home a whole week. Grandmother Lowell will come take care of Daddy and me and Lowell.

Miss Ruth gave me a Bible storybook of my own. It has easy words and lots of pictures. I asked Miss Ruth was there a picture of God in it, and she said no, 'cause nobody knows what God looks like.

The pictures of Jesus aren't real pictures like Daddy takes with his camera. They didn't have cameras when Jesus was a boy. People just draw pictures the way they think Jesus looked. Now maybe I won't get Jesus and God mixed up.

At Sunday school today Miss Gay told a Bible story about a little boy named Samuel. His mother and daddy wanted him so bad they prayed to Jesus for him. And Jesus sent them the dear little baby. When Samuel was about my size, he went to live at church all the time. Samuel prayed to Jesus. He did what Jesus wanted him to.

After Miss Gay finished the story, she asked, "Now, children, who was our story about?" And we all yelled, "SAM-U-EL!"

We played with blocks and toys that Miss Gay brought. They're hers. We dumped them on the floor. A girl played with us. She's thirteen years old, and her name is Ginger. She calls Miss Gay "Auntie." She likes to play with children. She wants to be a Sunday-school teacher. She played with Lowell mostly today. I told her Lowell was my little brother. She said he's cute.

She helped him build a train. I started to build a church, but Peter took my blocks and I didn't have enough. He was bad to me, so I was bad to him. When he built a garage, I knocked it over. Ginger didn't care.

When it was time to put the toys away, Miss Cora played loud on the piano. It made me feel like jumping around. We picked up the toys real fast and threw them into the box as hard as we could. We made noise just like the piano.

When I told Mommy and Daddy that Samuel prayed to Jesus, Mommy said we don't pray to Jesus—pray to God. Daddy said Samuel didn't know about Jesus, 'cause he was born hundreds of years before Jesus! Miss Gay didn't read her Bible well enough.

MOMMY GOES TO LAB
SCHOOL

23   You know what, we had waffles for breakfast this morning. Grandmother got up early and made them. And she let me wear the dress with blue lace. She said was I sure Mommy wouldn't mind, and I told her Mommy wouldn't care. (It's the first time I ever wore it to Sunday school.)

Mommy sent me a card from the lab school. It's beside a big lake. Children my size come there every day, and Mommy learns how to teach them. Miss Ruth is one of the teachers who shows Mommy how to teach.

It was so hot today that Miss Gay said we could play with the toys till time to have the lesson. Ginger wouldn't let anybody play with the doll except Patsy, 'cause Patsy is littlest.

Lowell stepped on my fingers, and he meant to, so I spanked his leg. Ginger said she'd tell my mother. I told her she couldn't 'cause my mother is away at lab school. Ginger kissed Lowell and held him on her lap.

I got tired just dumping toys, so I walked around the

room. Miss Gay stopped me—"Here, darling, you sit right down and draw Miss Gay a nice picture and color it."

Teachers always think you want to color a picture. But you get tired of coloring pictures. You want to do something else.

Teachers always ask you so many questions about your pictures. Miss Gay asked me, "What are you drawing, honey?" I told her I didn't know yet what it would be.

Now that they've already won their prize pins, there aren't so many children at Sunday school. Hughy doesn't come any more since his mother got mad.

We aren't going to have Sunday school for five Sundays. Then we'll have it again at the same time that other school starts. I'll go to everyday kindergarten and Sunday school both!

Miss Gay gave us all our old papers to take home and our cards with stars on them. I told her what the stars were for. The gold star was for the Lord's Prayer.

She said, "Children, let's hear you say the Lord's Prayer for Miss Gay."

You know what, we couldn't remember! Miss Gay started us, but we couldn't keep going. We don't know the Lord's Prayer any more.

Just before we went home, we sang, "This is the way we go to church so early in the morning." Wasn't that funny to sing go to church when we were really going home?

It was like a game. We went around the circle. Somebody in the middle showed what we do on Sunday morning, and we all did it. Gail showed comb her hair. Then she chose me to stand in the middle. I showed put on your shoes. Then I chose Miss Cora.

But Miss Cora said oh, no, and Miss Gay said to choose a child. Why can't teachers play like children and be "it" too?

Miss Gay kissed us all good-by, 'cause she won't be our teacher any more. I don't like for too many people to kiss me.

Outside the church Lowell saw Ginger. He pointed at her and yelled to Daddy, "There's my teacher, there's my teacher!"

The girls with Ginger laughed. Daddy said Ginger didn't look much older than a kindergartner herself.

24 PAINTED SUNSHINE

Whenever we play the game of what we want to do when we get big, Chucky always says drink coffee, shave, and go to everyday kindergarten.

In six more days he'll go to everyday kindergarten, and I'll go too. That's as many fingers and thumbs as I have on one hand and my thumb on the other hand. Joyce and Gail and Judy will be in everyday kindergarten too. Peter and Ellen will be in first grade.

When it's next Sunday, there will be Sunday school again. Daddy says he will be too tired to go. You know what, my daddy and Gail's daddy are painting our Sunday-school room!

Mommy learned about painting at lab school. Mommy learned so many things at lab school. Daddy thinks she knows too many things. He hasn't time to do them all. But he's not really mad. He laughs when he talks. Gail's daddy laughs too.

Mommy liked being at lab school. There were other mothers there who want to be Sunday-school teachers. Then there were some already-teachers who are mothers too. And there were some teachers like Miss Ruth who aren't mothers.

Some children who lived close to the lab school came to Sunday school every day. Mommy and the other mothers and teachers played with them and made things with them and learned things with them. They all had fun.

At night time the grownups went and sat by the lake and sang songs, and a man talked to them about God and about being teachers.

Mommy says she is glad now that she decided to be a Sunday-school teacher. The other day a lady came to ask her to belong to the garden club and the picture-taking club, but Mommy told her she won't have time.

Mommy and Mrs. Gordon and Dr. Hart talked a lot about the paint. Mr. Block didn't want new paint on our kindergarten room. He wanted to save it for the new church.

Dr. Hart found some money to buy paint, but not enough to pay real painters. So Daddy and Mr. Gordon are painting it free! Mommy and Mrs. Gordon and Miss Cora helped, too, on the low places.

Miss Cora will still be a helper at Sunday school. She doesn't quit when other teachers quit.

Gail and Lowell and I all painted one little place. We wanted to help some more, but Daddy said we were more help outdoors.

They painted the walls and the ceiling all pretty yellow. It's just like sunshine—like the real sunshine that can't get in.

Then Mommy said the floor looked bad. It needed paint too. And Mrs. Gordon said the tables and the chairs looked bad. And Miss Cora said the piano looked bad. They needed paint too.

Mommy said oh, my, before they painted the tables and chairs, the legs should be cut off some so they wouldn't be so tall for us. Mr. Mac helped Daddy and Mr. Gordon cut the legs.

Every day after supper Daddy and Mommy and Gail's mommy and daddy go over to the church to paint. Gail and Lowell and I play with Judy. Her house is right next to the church, 'cause her daddy is the preacher.

Mommy won't let us see the tables and chairs and piano yet. We don't even know what color they'll be. That's a surprise.

25 WE WERE GLAD

You know what, the chairs and tables and piano are blue! My favorite color. Not a shiny blue but a blue that's like the sky sometimes. The floor is brown like real floors in houses.

Mommy and Mrs. Gordon went over to the church yesterday and got everything ready just the way they wanted it for Sunday school.

When I saw the room this morning, I felt like I was in a different town. It looks bigger. Mommy asked me, "Do you like it?" and I said, "It's pretty." I wanted to say some more, but the words didn't talk.

I just walked around and looked. I touched the tables and the chairs and the piano. I sat down in one of the chairs. My feet touched flat on the floor. I looked up at the yellow ceiling. I was glad to be at Sunday school.

When all the children and their mothers and fathers came to the door, they said, "What a pretty room!"

Maribel said, "Is this the same room where we used to go to Sunday school?"

Mrs. Gordon put her arm on Maribel and told her she needed her to help choose some pictures to put up. There's a thing called wallboard that Daddy and Mr. Gordon fixed low on the wall. Maribel liked tacking pictures on it. One showed children going to church.

Maribel's mother asked, "Who did all this work?" and I told her.

She said she would have helped too, if she had known about it. She looked at the windows and asked Mrs. Gordon would she like to have some curtains. Mrs. Gordon said oh, yes. Maribel's mother likes to sew. She's going to make curtains.

Teachers in other rooms came to see us. They said, "When will somebody paint our rooms?"

Dr. Hart came to see us too. Mrs. Gordon asked would he stay with us for a while, and he did.

There were some new children just starting to our Sunday school. Mommy didn't want them to get lost trying to find our room. She told the man at the big door of the church that any boys and girls who haven't started to first grade should come down to our room. The first-graders went to another room.

Miss Cora wrote the names of the new children and their birthdays on cards. And you know what, we all wore tags around our necks with our names on them! That's so the teachers could read who we were instead of calling us "little girl in the yellow dress" and "little boy with the white shirt." Of course, Mommy and Mrs. Gordon and Miss Cora all knew who I was. It's fun to be somebody with your name on you.

When we were ready to go home, we took the tags off and left them with Miss Cora. They'll be ready for us next Sunday.

We played a game. We made a big circle, and Mrs. Gordon stood in the middle. She said, "I'm Mrs. Gordon, I see a girl named Joyce," and Joyce went to stand in the middle

with her. Mrs. Gordon called names till all the children were standing in the middle.

That is, all except a little new boy named Bruce. He didn't want to stand with the rest of us. Mrs. Gordon didn't make him. She let him sit on his mother's lap.

Then she said, "I see a min-is-ter named Dr. Hart."

"I see a helper named Mrs. Quick" (that's Mommy).

"I see a helper named Miss Cora."

Miss Cora went to the beautiful blue piano and played a song. It was about come to church. While Mrs. Gordon sang it, some of us found chairs and some of us sat on a blanket on the floor.

We talked—not just Mrs. Gordon, but all of us. About why we were glad to be at church. The gladdest we were was for the new-painted room. Mrs. Gordon told about the fathers who helped paint it. And lots of mothers and fathers gave money to buy paint and other things for the church.

Mrs. Gordon asked us how can we help. We'll wipe mud off our shoes before we come in. We'll keep our feet on the floor, not on the chairs or tables. We'll keep our crayons from making marks on the tables.

Mrs. Gordon felt like telling God we were glad about our

58

room. She said, "Thank you, God, for our happy time to-day."

And I'm going to have a happy time tomorrow, too! I start to everyday kindergarten! Maybe I'll tell God about that.

26 ⃞ EVERYBODY DID SOMETHING

Mommy doesn't use her typewriter very much. She's been too busy taking care of Lowell and me. But she used it the other day. She wrote a story about our Sunday-school kindergarten. And the man put it in the *Rose Leaf*. That's the paper a boy brings to our house.

Mommy wrote about our room and the paint and us kindergartners and did anybody have a rug or some toys to give us. And you know what, they did! A lady has to move back to the city, and her rug won't fit her other house, She doesn't go to our church, but she likes little boys and girls.

More than one people called Mommy about the toys. Mommy took the ones she wanted—a doll buggy and a doll bed and a doll high chair and a little train and a little fire engine. A man who has a place where they cut pieces of wood will make some big blocks nice and smooth for us to build with.

Gail and Joyce and I said we'd each leave one of our dolls at Sunday school—not our very favorite ones.

Then Mommy went to the city and bought storybooks and great big crayons and sheets of paper and an easel to paint pictures on. I asked her to get the easel 'cause we have one in everyday kindergarten and I like it.

Mr. Broshaw said Mommy and Mrs. Gordon could buy things. They went to a meeting, and all the teachers in the whole Sunday school were there. Dr. Hart was there too. He and Mr. Broshaw asked the teachers to tell what they'd like to have. And the teachers decided we're not going upstairs with the big people any more. They think it's better for us in our own rooms.

Daddy asked Mommy, "Now where will you keep all these storybooks and things?"

Mommy said oh, my! And I said the other teachers used to put things on the piano.

Yesterday Mommy and Mrs. Gordon went to church to see Mr. Mac. Gail and I went too. They asked him could he find a cupboard anywhere. He took us to a dark place on the other side of the furnace. You know what, there was an old cupboard! Mr. Mac doesn't know how it got there.

We cleaned it out. Gail and I threw things in the wastebasket. Mommy and Mrs. Gordon kept laughing and saying, "Look at this!" There was a calendar for when Mommy was born. There were real, real, real old Sunday-school papers with funny pictures of boys with long black stockings, and pants tied around their knees.

There were pictures of babies pasted on a baby bed who are grown up now. Mommy saved those pictures. One of them was Mr. Block's boy. His name was Roger Block, Junior.

There's enough blue paint left to paint the cupboard.

While we were at church, Mrs. Gordon and Mommy and Gail and I got our room ready. We put the toys in one corner and the books on a table and fixed the easel ready to paint. Gail and I wished we could stay and play.

They took the purple altar out. Mrs. Gordon said it's not the right kind for kindergartners. Instead, we have a little low table that she brought from home. We'll put the Bible and pretty pictures on it.

I asked where was Mrs. Wright's flannelboard. She took

it with her. But Mrs. Gordon says we'll do something better than the flannelboard—we'll pretend we're the story people ourselves.

This morning she put some red flowers on the little table. I saw them as soon as I went in. We could touch them and smell them, and she didn't mind.

I painted on the easel. It wasn't any special picture. I liked using the different colors. While I was painting, Waldo came in. He wanted to paint on the easel too. I told him he'd have to wait, 'cause I was there first.

Everybody found something to do. We can even go to the cupboard and get games and crayons ourselves. Nobody just sat on a chair and sat. Sunday school started as soon as you got there.

Bruce sat on a chair, but he looked at the books. His mother read to him, and he wasn't afraid. I listened some of the time.

I have new boy friends and girl friends now that I go to everyday kindergarten—Donna and Joan and Kenneth and Jay. They come to my Sunday school, too. We told Mrs. Gordon we are in all the same schools. Sometimes we forget and call her Miss Conley! Miss Conley is our everyday teacher. Mrs. Gordon laughs when we do it. And we laugh.

Peter and Ellen wish they were still in our Sunday school room instead of first grade. They came in this morning to see our toys.

Why, our room is like a house to live in now!

27 WE'LL TAKE GOOD CARE

Today we wrote a letter to Mrs. Epstein. She's the lady that gave us the rug. Waldo came in while we were writing it. Mrs. Gordon really wrote the words, but we told her what to say. We said:

"Dear Mrs. Epstein: Thank you for the rug. We like to play on it. We're sitting on it right now."

Then Chucky thought we should write to the man who gave us the blocks. Chucky likes the blocks better than anything. We said to the block man:

"Thank you for the blocks you gave us. They are good blocks. We like to build things with them."

We have more room now. The little kids like Lowell and Patsy that are three years old aren't in our way any more. They go to Mrs. Hart's house and have Sunday school. It's the nursery department. Mrs. Hart is their teacher. Lowell likes it. All the time at home whenever I tell about Miss Conley, Lowell says, "Mrs. Hart is my teacher." She gave him a book with pictures and little stories in it, and when people come to our house, Lowell shows it to them and says, "See my Sunday-school book." Daddy reads it to him.

We wore our names around our necks again this morning, but Mrs. Gordon thinks we won't do it any more, 'cause now she knows us. Miss Cora put the tags on us. Right at the door she has a table that folds up. When we come in, she looks for our name in her little book. Then she doesn't have to call our names out loud the way she used to.

The basket for our money is on her table, too, and we drop it in right away. Then we won't lose it while we're playing. After Miss Cora is through with her table, she folds it up so it won't be in our way.

This morning Bruce let his mother leave. Mommy showed her upstairs to the mothers' class. Mrs. Gordon tells all the mothers not to stay too many times, so now we don't have them in our room talking about us. She took Bruce around the room to look at things. She said maybe I could show him the new little stove, and I did.

Miss Cora made it. It's a box painted white and turned upside down. She painted black things on the front for turning on the gas and on top for setting pans on to cook.

Bruce and I played cooking dinner. Miss Cora watched. I told her it was a nice stove. She smiled. She is more smiley than she used to be.

When we were through playing with our toys, Mrs. Gordon had something to tell us: If we make too much noise, it dis-turbs (I like the new words she helps us learn) the other rooms. She asked Miss Cora, "Do you think if you played some soft music, it would help us put our toys away quietly?"

Miss Cora *did* play music that made your feet walk easy and your hands put the blocks on the shelves click, click, not BANG, BANG. We have a pretty blue wastebasket to throw scraps in instead of on the floor.

Then we sat down on the rug. Mommy and Miss Cora sat on it too, just like us. Mrs. Gordon was happy that we were such quiet helpers.

She had a box beside her, but we couldn't see what was in it. She'd show us later. First we talked about our money in the basket. She asked us what it was for. Some of us said for Jesus, and some said for God. But we don't really give it *to* them. Mrs. Gordon told us that it buys books and crayons and papers that help us to learn about Jesus and God. It pays for coal to keep our church warm. We looked in our basket, and it wasn't just pennies. There were other pieces of money. We won't call it our "pennies" any more. We'll call it our "offering." We learned what "offering" means. It's "giving."

Joyce's daddy goes around to all the rooms and gets the money and puts it in a big bank. Then when it's time to spend the money, he takes it out. He's spending some for our kindergarten right now! That's what was in the box. New books—one for each one of us to take home to keep —our very own! It's about friends.

When Mrs. Gordon could see all our eyes—she doesn't talk to us till she sees our eyes—she held up one of the new books, and you know what, our own money and our fathers' and mothers' money pay for the books. So we'll take very good care of them and read them at home. There are prayers in the book. One of them says thank you to God for dinner.

Mrs. Gordon read it to us. Her voice makes you want to listen. And then she bowed her head and said, "Dear God, we're happy to have new books. Help us to take good care of them."

I bowed my head too.

Now Mommy and Daddy can both stay sometimes for church to hear Dr. Hart preach. Lowell and I can play in our kindergarten room with other children. Miss Cora told Mommy she doesn't think it will work. They tried a nursery one time, and not enough mothers helped. They always forgot. But Mrs. Hart told Mommy the way she's doing it. She wrote the mothers' names down, and she calls them when it's their turn to help. She wants to find the same mothers for every Sunday, though, instead of changing.

Jay's mother and Joan's mother were the ones there today. Mrs. Hart talked to them. She said we could do things like in real Sunday school instead of playing all the time. I get a little tired of just playing. So I finished painting a picture that I started in Sunday school.

The best part I like is the food—crackers and juice. You get hungry when you're at church two times.

28 CURTAINS FROM MARIBEL

Guess what, Waldo was on time this morning! He beat me to the easel.

I can say the little prayer in my Sunday-school book when we eat dinner. Today I said it real nice, 'cause we had Swiss steak and cheese potatoes. Lowell wants to say it too.

Last night he begged, "Let me do it." You know what he prayed? "Hi diddle dumpling, my son John, went to bed with his stockings on."

Whenever Daddy reads to me out of my Sunday-school book, Lowell brings his book and says, "Daddy, read." He wants to do everything I do.

There's a magazine for the mothers and fathers and teachers to read, too. Mrs. Gordon wants all of them to come to a meeting next Thursday night. This morning she told us to tell our mothers and daddies. They're to watch for a letter in the mail. But my mother already knows about it!

Mommy fixed a place on our bookshelves for our Sunday-school books and her magazine and Bible and my Bible storybook that Miss Ruth gave me. Mommy forgot once, and I found her magazine on the kitchen table! I have to be careful to put my book away so Lowell will learn to put his away too.

We had a new boy in our room today. His name is Roger Block the Third. His daddy is in the Army, and he and his mother have come to live with his Grandpa and Grandma Block. Grandpa Block brought Roger and his mother to our room. The grandpa said they didn't have toys in Sunday school when he was a boy. They learned the Bible.

Mommy had something to show Mr. Block and Roger's mother. She brought the old pictures of the babies on the baby bed that we found in the cupboard. Mr. Block laughed and pointed to one picture. It was his own boy when he was a baby—Roger Block, Junior, the one that's in the Army. Little Roger looked at his daddy-that-was-a-baby. Then we all wanted to look. Mommy gave the picture to Roger's mother, and she was glad.

She stayed to visit. Roger liked the toys. He ran right over to the fire engine. Kenneth was playing with it, and he said, "You can't have it. I had it first!"

Kenneth held on tight. Mrs. Gordon sat down beside him and said, "Kenneth is the fire chief. A fire chief always has firemen to help him put out fires, doesn't he?"

Kenneth said there wasn't any fire. So Mrs. Gordon asked Chucky could his block house be afire, and Chucky said it could. Then Kenneth and Roger drove the truck over to put out the fire.

It's fun when Mrs. Gordon plays with us. She doesn't play all the time. Just sometimes.

You know what, Ginger wanted to come back and play with us. Her mother asked Mommy, and Mommy said she wasn't old enough. Ginger's mother said Ginger was a baby sitter, so why couldn't she be a Sunday-school teacher? Mommy told her that being a Sunday-school teacher for kindergartners is one of the grown-uppest jobs there is.

While we sat on the rug and talked this morning, Maribel had a surprise for us. She opened a box—the curtains her mother made for our room. They're so pretty! They have a little boy sailing a boat and a girl throwing a ball on them.

We helped put them up at the windows. Mrs. Gordon showed us how to push them on the curtain sticks. It was fun. We held them for her and Miss Cora while they climbed up. Miss Cora was very careful, 'cause she didn't want to fall and hurt her ankle any more the way she did before.

Mrs. Gordon pushed the curtains back so we can still see out the windows, only we can't really see anything. She lifted Maribel up to help push the curtains, and Maribel said, "I can see the grass!"

Miss Cora thought of a good idea: if we just had something to stand on under the windows, we could see grass all the time.

We told Mrs. Gordon we'd remember to say thank you to Maribel's mother when she came after Maribel. I did remember. And then some of the others remembered. I said, "Thank you for the curtains."

Maribel's mother looked smiley. Maribel likes Sunday school now.

29 THE RED BIBLE

Miss Cora said they wouldn't come. And they didn't. The fathers and mothers. To the meeting. At least not many.

Mommy felt so sad. Daddy told her she looked like she had lost a million-dollar case. That's what he always says when she doesn't have a smiley look.

Mrs. Gordon came over, and she didn't have a smiley look either. And when Gail and I turned the milk bottle over in the refrigerator, they scolded like mothers do when they're tired. They made us sit down. But we weren't tired. We just listened.

They don't know why more fathers and mothers didn't come. Mrs. Gordon sent letters to all of them. Some of them told her they couldn't come 'cause they didn't have anybody to stay with the baby. That made Mrs. Gordon mad. The people will get a baby sitter so they can go to a party, but they wouldn't get one so they could come to her meeting.

Donna's mother called and said why did the children play all the time at Sunday school? She wants Donna to learn the Bible. But she didn't come to the meeting. She went to a flower show.

Mrs. Gordon wanted to give the mothers and fathers their magazines and tell them what to read to their own selves and to their children.

She was glad about one thing. The mothers who were there promised to cut pictures out of big magazines for us. She gave them colored paper to paste the pictures on.

She was glad about another thing. Waldo's mother was there. She said Waldo never liked Sunday school before was why he was always late. Now he makes them get up early!

After a while Mommy and Mrs. Gordon started smiling again, and Mommy told us to come to the kitchen and we'd all have a tea party. While we were eating, Mrs. Gordon said, you know what, they should have had a tea party instead of just a meeting. Mommy said yes. That's what they'll do next time.

Mommy will write a letter to Miss Ruth and ask her about it. She told me she was sorry she was cross about the milk bottle. I like it when mothers are sorry.

When we got to Sunday school this morning, there was a picture of our own church on our pretty table—that's what I call the table Mrs. Gordon puts things on.

First I played with the jigsaw puzzle. It's new. Miss Cora made it. She pasted a picture on cardboard and then cut it into pieces. Miss Cora can do lots of things now. Sometimes Mrs. Gordon helps her.

I put the puzzle together all by myself. It was a church with a bell on top. Then Judy put it together. We did it better than Joyce.

Mrs. Gordon asked Chucky if he could build a church

with the blocks to look like our church. He tried. Then Roger built one too.

Before we put away our toys, Mrs. Gordon let all of us look at the churches Chucky and Roger built. Chucky wished he could build one big enough to go inside. Mrs. Gordon will see if she can find a big one.

After we sat down on the rug, she asked if we had seen a picture of a church in the room. I knew where it was— on the pretty table—and so did some of the others. But she doesn't let us talk all at one time. She chose Joan to come stand beside her. Joan pointed to the picture of our own church.

Mrs. Gordon told us that a long time ago the people who lived in Rose Park built this church. Now it's getting old and it isn't big enough, so the people who live here now want to build a new church. It takes hundreds and hundreds of dollars, and there isn't enough money yet.

Then Mrs. Gordon let Judy come stand by her and tell why we go to church. Judy said to learn about God.

Mrs. Gordon took a book off the table, and we didn't know what it was. It was a red book. Guess what, it was the Bible! I thought the Bible could only be black. But this one is red and looks just like a real book.

Mrs. Gordon opened it and showed it to us. Then she read about going to church. It's the same verse I heard once before, only it doesn't have the "unto" in it. She read it two times, just like Miss Conley does—slow-like so each word stands up by itself.

She asked would anybody else like to read the verse. We wanted to. I stood by her and she showed me where the words were in the Bible. I acted like I was reading them:

> I was glad when they said to me,
> "Let us go to the house of the Lord!"

69

When we were through reading, Mrs. Gordon put the picture of our church in the Bible right where the verse is. Now I know why we call the church the house of the Lord. Lord is God's other name. And the church is the place where we hear stories about God. God doesn't really live just in the church though. He lives everywhere. Mrs. Gordon told us.

When Daddy came to the kindergarten room, I showed him the red Bible. I showed him how I could read it. I said, "Get us a Bible like this, Daddy." So he looked at it. After we got home, I asked him some more. Maybe tomorrow he will buy us a red Bible for our own house.

30 FOR ALL THE PEOPLE

Stories are nice, but you know what, you don't always have to have a story at Sunday school. We didn't have any today. We did things.

That's why I like Sunday school now. Mrs. Gordon lets us do other things than sing "Jesus Loves Me" and draw pictures and listen.

Sometimes we work at tables, but we can sit at any one we want. And all the tables don't have to do the same thing. We're not in classes any more the way we were with Mrs. Wright. Today we didn't use the tables, 'cause we had something else. They were stacked against the wall.

We had a church big enough to crawl in! But it's not the church Mommy found. Daddy and I have a joke on her.

Mommy looked out our window and saw Mrs. Spencer getting a television. It was in a great big box. The television man left the box in the yard. Mommy said, "Kathy Ann, that would be just right for our play church."

Mrs. Spencer hasn't been mad at Y'honor for a while, so Mommy asked her for the box. Mrs. Spencer said yes.

Mrs. Gordon thought it was nice too. Lowell and Gail and I played with it in our yard till Mommy said they'd better take it to the church before we broke it.

It stuck 'way out of the car trunk. Gail and I held the church doors while Mommy and Mrs. Gordon carried it in. But you know what, when they got to the door of our room, the box was too big. It wouldn't go through! They turned it and turned it. Then they laughed. Mommy won't ever say she's a smart mother any more.

There wasn't anything else to do with the box but bring it back to our yard. Gail thought why couldn't we make an outdoor church. Mommy helped us put a steeple on it made out of cardboard.

Joyce came over, and she wanted to help. I said she couldn't, 'cause it was ours. Mommy stopped putting the steeple on. She said she couldn't help build a church that wasn't for all the people who wanted to come. God wants everybody to be happy at church, just like the man in the Bible who said, "I was glad when they said to me, 'Let us go to the house of the Lord!' "

I felt sorry about Joyce. I let her play too.

We took crayons and drew windows on the box. When Daddy came home, he cut a door for us. Now there's snow, and it's fun to crawl inside.

Mrs. Gordon read in a book about another kind of church. When we got to Sunday school this morning, it was all ready for us to work on. We used orange boxes— two at each corner—one on top of the other.

What could be put over it to make a church? Kenneth guessed paper. That was right. Mrs. Gordon had brown paper like you wrap things in. She laid it on the floor.

Some wanted a stone church, but more of us wanted brick. Brick won. We used crayons to draw the bricks. Miss Cora helped us cut two windows. Then we pasted cellophane on them, and they looked like real church windows. I let Roger paste with me—he's only four.

It took all of us to stretch the paper around the orange boxes and on top. Chucky struck some tacks in. We didn't put any paper in front. That's the door.

Mrs. Gordon asked what else should our church have. Judy wanted a steeple. Where her daddy used to preach, the church had a steeple and a bell in it. Next Sunday Mrs. Gordon will try to find us a steeple and a bell.

Jay thought we should have chairs in our church. Of course you couldn't put real chairs in, but we put big blocks in. And there was room for Joyce and Gail and Chucky and me all to go in at one time. We took turns till everybody had a chance to go in and sit down.

You know what, you can *sing* a prayer. We sang one—

> For my church I'm glad today,
> Thank you, God, our Father.

We did so many things—that's why there wasn't any time for a story. Mrs. Gordon doesn't all the time say "hurry, hurry" and look at her watch. We stop Sunday school nice and quiet. The fathers and mothers can't come in till we're through.

When Roger's Grandpa Block came to get him, he asked in his big voice, "What did you learn today?" And Roger showed him our brick church.

▣ 31 KNOCK, KNOCK!

Daddy *did* buy one of the red Bibles. We keep it on the shelf with our Sunday-school books. I asked Daddy to find me the place where it says, "I was glad when they said to me." It took him a long time.

Lowell knows the dinner-table prayer now. We take turns. I told Daddy he should have a turn too. He looked for one in the red Bible. Today he read it to us before we ate our fried chicken. It was too long. I wanted the drumstick.

Every Sunday will be Daddy's turn. But he won't read too long any more.

Daddy jokes Mommy. He says if she keeps on teaching Sunday school, she will make everybody so good that there won't be any bad people for the lawyers to work for.

Mommy and Mrs. Gordon have been visiting the mothers. They go in the mornings when Gail and I are at kindergarten. Lowell goes with them. He is good when he's by himself. Mommy and Mrs. Gordon give the mothers the magazines and tell them what we do at Sunday school.

Donna's mother doesn't like the magazine. Yesterday I

73

was standing in line with Mommy at the store, and the lady with the basket right in front of us was Donna's mother. She told Mommy she read the magazine. She likes the Bible stories in it, but she doesn't like some of the other stories—the one about Bushy Squirrel and the nuts. She wants Donna to have just Bible stories at Sunday school.

Mommy told her that God takes care of Bushy Squirrel. That's why he's in the Sunday-school stories. But Donna's mother still doesn't like Bushy Squirrel.

And she doesn't like for us to play at Sunday school. Mommy tried to tell her that we learn to be good by playing together, but Donna's mother just threw her potatoes and squashes out of the basket.

Donna, though, liked for Mommy and Mrs. Gordon to visit her mother. At Sunday school today she ran up to Mrs. Gordon and said, "You came to my house, didn't you?"

Mrs. Gordon didn't forget the steeple and the bell. This morning we put them on. We set a box on top of the orange crates, and Miss Cora tied a bell in it. She said why couldn't we sing the bells song that's in the book.

First she played it on the piano. Mrs. Gordon showed us how to hum it. She told the words just like a story. Then she sang it by herself—the whole thing—while we listened. It was such an easy song that we learned it right away:

> Hear the Church bells ringing,
> This is what they say:
> Fathers, Mothers, Children,
> Come to Church today;
> Ding! Dong! Ding! Dong! Ding! Dong! Ding! [1]

Jay rang the real little bell in our paper brick church,

[1] From *Learning in the Church Kindergarten*, Part III, p. 127. Used by permission.

and the rest of us pretended to ring bells with our hands. We sang so well that Mrs. Gordon told us another song about "Friends, Friends, Friends." She said wouldn't it be lonely if we went to Sunday school some morning and we were the only one there! We like to be with our friends.

We heard a story about a boy named Carl who went to church. He played with his friends in the kindergarten, and then they walked all over the church. They went knock, knock on a door, and there was the minister. Mrs. Gordon asked who is our minister, and I said Dr. Hart.

Judy said, "That's my daddy!"

Chucky said, "My daddy knows Dr. Hart."

Joan said, "My daddy is an umpire for the boys' team."

Mrs. Gordon lets us help her tell stories. She said yes, all our daddies are helpers. Carl, the little boy in the story, and his friends went knock, knock on another door, and it was the lady who played the organ.

But we didn't know who plays our organ, 'cause she wasn't anybody's mother in our room. Mrs. Gordon had to tell us. It's Mrs. Terry.

Knock, knock on another door, and Carl found the man who took care of the church. We knew who that was, even if he isn't anybody's father in our room. Mr. Mac.

After the story, we did a new kind of drawing. There was a long, long piece of white paper tacked on the wall where we could reach it. Any of us who wanted to could draw pictures on it of people or things we like at church.

It was fun. Chucky drew the little church. Judy drew her own daddy. Maribel drew the curtains her mother made. All our little pictures made one long picture. You call it a "mural."

Mrs. Gordon talked to each one of us about ours. She wanted all of us to look at Maribel's—it was so good.

When she came to mine, she said, "Now, Kathy Ann, tell us about your picture."

I didn't say anything. She asked me, "Is it one of our helpers at church?"

And then I told her. "It's you."

Mrs. Gordon put her arm around me and hugged me. I felt like I was in a different town.

32 ⬛ THEY WERE FRIENDS

This morning when I got to Sunday school, I didn't feel like building with blocks or drawing pictures or looking at books. I felt like playing in the doll corner. And that's what Judy and I did. We waked the dolls up and told them it was time for breakfast. I made mine drink her orange juice before she could have her bacon and egg. I cooked on the little box stove.

Mrs. Gordon came by to visit us. She had on a new blouse. I told her it was pretty, and she said, "Thank you." I like teachers who look nice. I wish I had gold hair like Mrs. Gordon.

She asked us would we bring our children to Sunday school. We had to hurry fast, 'cause we had to put clean clothes on the dolls. We didn't have time to wash the dishes.

We took our children to the play church. We sat down on the block seats, and Judy said there should be a preacher in front like her daddy. So she quit being a mother and was the preacher. Then I was the Sunday-school teacher and Judy was one of the children.

Mrs. Gordon peeked in and asked if we'd like to read out of the red Bible. I was very careful with it. Donna and Jay came in. Then it was time for our play Sunday school to be over. I said, "Dear God, thank you for a nice time." That's what I say when I go home from parties.

At clean-up time Judy and I put the dolls away and swept the floor. We did it just like the children in the picture Miss Cora tacked up over our doll corner.

Today we did something like Carl, the boy in the story last Sunday. We went to see Mr. Mac in his workroom back of the furnace. He showed us inside the furnace, where the fire burns. While we're still asleep in bed, he comes over to make the fire so our room will be nice and warm for Sunday school.

Then we saw the brooms and the sweeper and the dust-rags that Mr. Mac uses to clean up the church. Every Saturday when we're playing, he works to get the church ready for us.

Mr. Mac let us look at his tool box, too. That's what Chucky liked. Just as soon as he can find time, Mr. Mac is going to make us something with those tools. He walked down the hall to show us. It's to be a thing for our wraps that can be set out in the hall instead of in our room. It will have low hangers so we can hang up our own coats.

We asked Mr. Mac to come into our room and hear us sing. We sang "Friends, Friends, Friends," 'cause he's one of our friends. We showed him our little church, and he said he'd been very careful of it when he cleaned our room.

After Mr. Mac left, we talked about how we can help him take care of the church. He's kind of old, like a grandpa, and it's hard for him to pick up things. We'll pick up our crayons and our blocks, and we'll put our scraps in the waste-basket.

I liked the story Mrs. Gordon told us today. She doesn't read stories out of books. She talks them. But she held the red Bible open on her lap, for it was a Bible story. It was an easy story, too. I can remember it.

It was about Jesus. Some fathers and mothers took their boys and girls to see Jesus. They were all so happy. But when they got to the place where Jesus was, one of the men said, "Go 'way, Jesus hasn't time for children."

(I'm so glad Jesus heard him!) Jesus said, "Yes, I do too have time for children. Let them come see me."

So the children and their mothers and fathers went up close to Jesus, and he took turns holding the little ones on his lap and he told them stories. They all had a happy day. I felt just like I was there too.

Mrs. Gordon held up the picture that was on the pretty table. Jay said it was Jesus teaching the Sunday-school class. And Mrs. Gordon said yes, it was like a Sunday-school class when Jesus talked to the children that day.

Mrs. Gordon had a smaller picture of Jesus and the children, too, and she put that one in the Bible where the story is.

I would have been the little girl sitting on his lap. I sit on Daddy's lap that way. I think Jesus was kind of like my daddy.

Jesus was the children's friend. And you know what else I think? I think Jesus and God were friends.

33 GOD PLANNED IT

We took our little church down. There wasn't room for it to stay up all the time. Sometimes you get tired of things anyway. You like new things.

Today we had new things. We had food! A can of peaches and a can of peas and a little bottle of milk and a loaf of bread and puffed wheat. We ate the puffed wheat!

I saw the food on the table as soon as I got to Sunday

school. Maribel saw it too. Maribel talks now. She asked Mrs. Gordon were we going to have a party.

Mrs. Gordon said maybe we might have a pretend party. She had paper plates and pictures of things to eat, all pretty colors. Kenneth knew what they were. His daddy has a book like that to tell him what to plant in his garden. You call it a catalogue. There were magazines, too, like Mommy and Daddy read.

We began to cut out pictures to paste on the plates to play "eat dinner." Mrs. Gordon remembered that little brothers and sisters like bright pictures like those. She wondered if the nursery children over at Mrs. Hart's house had a picture book of things to eat. Judy didn't think they did.

Mrs. Gordon picked up some sheets of orange paper. She asked what could we do with them? And I knew! We could paste the pictures on the sheets and make a picture book for the nursery. I said I ought to be one to help, 'cause my little brother is in the nursery department.

Maribel and Judy and I decided we'd rather make the book than fix the paper plates, so we worked together. Miss Cora gave us a wet rag to wipe paste off our hands, and she helped us put the pictures on straight. We let her cut out some pictures too. It's fun when the teacher does things *with* you. Miss Cora is more fun-like than she used to be.

Maribel and Judy and I are all five years old, so we can do good work now. We tried to keep the pages from being messy. I pasted on a picture of bananas. Lowell just loves bananas.

While we made the book for the nursery, some other children pasted food in the paper plates and played eat dinner. Mrs. Gordon visited them, and they gave her some dinner. Donna took a plate over to where the dolls were and fed them.

Mommy sat at the storybook table. I went over sometimes to see what she was reading to Bruce and Joan. One of the books was about Farmer Brown, and it had pictures of the things that grew on his farm.

We didn't quite finish our nursery book. We'll put a cover on it next Sunday and take it over to the nursery.

When we put our work away and went to the rug, Mrs. Gordon was holding the can of peaches and the loaf of bread and singing. Mrs. Gordon doesn't always do the same way every Sunday. You always wonder.

The song was about all good things to eat. She sang it two times, and then we helped her. She doesn't make us sing real loud.

She said suppose we couldn't talk. How could we show someone what we were singing about? That was fun. For things to eat we put our hands up to our mouth. For work we went snip, snip like scissors, and for play we jumped. For flowers we pretended to hold a bunch to smell. We made rain fall with our fingers and a round sun with our arms. At the last we bowed our heads for thank you to God.

Another day we'll sing the words and do them at the same time.

We talked about the food on the table. Mrs. Gordon asked us why we thanked God for it, and Chucky told her—'cause God gives it to us. Mrs. Gordon said yes, in the very beginning God made a plan for the whole world. He knew people would get hungry, so he fixed it for food to grow.

We knew how the can of peas grew. Somebody like Kenneth's daddy planted the seed in the dirt, and it grew into plants with peas on them. Then somebody picked them, and somebody cooked them and put them in cans—the way Maribel's mother does.

But you don't plant a bottle for milk! You get it from the milkman. And he gets it from the farmer. And the farmer gets it from the cows. We've talked about that at everyday kindergarten. God planned for cows to give milk.

Then Mrs. Gordon showed us some little seeds. Nobody knew what they were. They're what you make flour out of. Wheat. The farmer plants the seeds, and they grow and make more seeds on the end of long things like grass. Mrs. Gordon asked Bruce to show us a picture of wheat—it was in the book Mommy read to him and Joan.

After the wheat is ground up into flour, you can make bread out of it. But all the wheat isn't ground up. Some is made into cereal like the puffed wheat.

You know what, a lot of people help God. He sends the sunshine and the rain to make things grow, but the farmer and the milkman and the canners and the cookers and the grocers all help. That's the way God planned it. I think he was pretty smart. Mrs. Gordon read us a book about God's plan—with pictures.

The Bible tells about God's plan too. It tells us to give thanks. Mrs. Gordon read it in the red Bible—"We give thanks, O God, we give thanks."

Miss Cora and Mommy gave us paper cups with puffed

wheat in them. Before we ate it, we remembered, "We give thanks, O God, we give thanks."

34 EVERYBODY TOLD

Guess what, Maribel brought a can of her mother's tomatoes to Sunday school today! Her mother came in and told Mrs. Gordon that Maribel just begged to bring it. Mrs. Gordon was so glad. Maribel's daddy raised the tomatoes in his garden, and her mother canned them, so they both helped God.

Maribel's mother isn't a bad mother after you know her more.

Mrs. Gordon set the can on the table for us to look at. She asked how would we like a treasure box where we could bring things to show. Those of us who are five years old know about that. We have one at everyday kindergarten, and whoever brings something shows and tells.

Mommy thought maybe we could make a treasure box out of one of the orange crates we used in our little church. She went right home and got one.

She and Gail and Waldo covered it with yellow crepe paper, and it looks pretty. Maribel set the can of tomatoes on the shelf part.

She and Judy and I and Miss Cora finished the nursery book. We pasted a picture of a little boy just Lowell's size on the front. We put on our coats and went over to Judy's house, where the nursery department is.

When we got there, we couldn't think what to say, so Miss Cora told Mrs. Hart. Mrs. Hart said thank you very much, that the little ones would like our book. She showed it to them right then, and they knew the names of the pictures. Lowell ran up to me and told the others, "She's my sister." I felt nice.

Today we sang and we did the words of our thank-you song. Then we played a game. Mrs. Gordon started, "I am a little squirrel. What food am I thankful for?" The one who answered first got to be it. When it was my turn, I said, "I am a little doggie. What am I thankful for?"

God planned for animals to have food too. But people have to help. If I didn't feed Y'honor, he'd get sick.

Guess who told a story at Sunday school—Mommy! It was a good story, too. It was the one about Bushy Squirrel. Bushy lived in Margaret's yard. One day she saw him running up the tree with his face all puffed up like he had mumps. But he didn't have mumps.

He was carrying nuts and hiding them in a hole in the tree to eat next winter. Margaret put some walnuts out on the porch. Then she peeked out the window to see what Bushy would do. Sure enough, he came and got the walnuts and carried them up the tree. He went "Squeak, squeak," and Margaret thought he was saying, "Thank you, Margaret."

God needs us to help him take care of the animals, specially in the wintertime. We can put bread out for the birds if there's snow on the ground.

(Daddy says Mommy is turning into a squirrel. She saves everything for her Sunday-school box—pictures and string and empty cans and spools.)

Thanksgiving is coming again! We talked about it today. My Grandmother and Grandfather Lowell and the others will be at our house this time. I told Mrs. Gordon. Everybody told. Kenneth's big brother is coming home from college for Thanksgiving.

We can help fix the Thanksgiving dinner table. We can make little cards that have people's names on them so they know where to sit. Mrs. Gordon showed us one already made. It's a piece of orange paper folded so it stands up. And there's a candy mint—the kind in paper—stuck on each one with sticky tape.

Miss Cora had the things all on the tables for us to work. We could choose little pictures of food to paste on, or we could draw pictures on our cards. I'm going to make all of mine different. Today I made Grandmother's and Grandfather's and Aunt Sue's. Miss Cora wrote the names on for us. The mints look good. But I didn't eat any.

There was a sack for each one of us to put our cards in. We left them at Sunday school so we can work on them again next Sunday.

35 POOR CHILDREN ARE REAL

You know what, my daddy is on a committee. A committee is to go to meetings. It's the committee to build a new church. Dr. Hart asked Daddy to be on it 'cause he's a lawyer. Mr. Block is the boss of the committee. He wants lots of colored windows in the new church. But he doesn't want too many Sunday-school rooms for children.

That makes Mommy mad. She tells Daddy to tell Mr. Block. Daddy says Mr. Block doesn't like to be told.

Roger Block the Third told something today. He brought a coconut. His daddy sent it from 'way far off. It doesn't look like coconuts in the store. It has a funny shell. Roger put it on top of our treasure box till show-and-tell time. When his mother came, they took it home. She said Roger talked ever since last Sunday about bringing a treasure to show.

Coconut has milk inside it. You can hear it shake. Everybody had a turn shaking. It's not like the milk from cows, but it's good to drink. Mrs. Gordon was so glad Roger brought the coconut, 'cause she had something to tell us about another kind of milk. Powdered milk.

She showed us. You add water to it and make lots of milk. You can have milk even where there isn't any milkman. You can give it to children who haven't any milk. That's what we are going to do.

I found out something—poor children are real! Today I saw a picture of them. And Mrs. Gordon told us a story about them. A true story.

They are little children the size of Lowell. Their mothers can't stay home and take care of them, 'cause they have to go to work. Some of the daddies are sick and the mothers work to get money. The mothers leave the little children in a nursery while they're at work.

The nursery is in a building with toys, and a lady takes care of the children. They eat lunch at a table. They aren't as big and strong as we are, 'cause they don't have as much food as we have to eat.

Waldo wanted to know why doesn't God give them food. Mrs. Gordon ex-plained (I learned that word at school) that God does plan enough food for everybody, but he needs helpers to see that everybody gets his share.

One of the things the children in the nursery need is milk. They like powdered milk. And we're going to give them some! For Thanksgiving.

We can buy it our own selves with real money. We have a little store in our room. Today we used play money. Mrs. Gordon gave us some boxes and cans to sell. Next Sunday she'll have real cans of powdered milk for us to buy. Then we'll send them to the children at the nursery.

Miss Cora had paper cans for us to take home. There was a letter on them for the mothers to read. It told about the powdered milk. Miss Cora will mail them to the ones who weren't there today.

I made dinner-table cards for my cousins Keith and Janet today. Our room looks like Thanksgiving. We have pictures all around. They're pictures the mothers cut out and pasted on colored paper. Maribel's mother brought them this morning. Mommy put them low down on the wall where we could look at them and talk about them.

Some smaller pictures pasted on colored paper are in little flat boxes. We mustn't mix the boxes up. I looked at one this morning. It had pictures of wheat and the things you make from wheat—just like we talked about one Sunday.

We made a big circle and played the farmer game. First we plowed the ground. Then we made nice straight rows to drop the seeds in. I planted wheat. Joyce planted corn. We turned our arms into a round sun and our fingers into raindrops falling down. My wheat grew up and I cut it. We all pretended to stack our food in the middle of the circle.

Mrs. Gordon said, "I feel like thanking God for farmers." I felt like it too. I bowed my head and I said the words inside myself with her: "Thank you, God, for farmers."

She always prays to "God," so I don't get mixed up with the names. I think she knows him real well.

When we had our wraps on, Miss Cora gave us the paper cans. Mrs. Gordon said to each one, "Be sure to tell Mother and Daddy about the powdered milk." But of course my mother already knew.

36 WE PLAY TAKE THE MILK

Mommy was the storekeeper today. She put boxes on top of each other like shelves in a real store. The cans of powdered milk were in the boxes.

But before we bought milk for the everyday-nursery children, we needed something to put it in. We covered a basket with orange and brown paper. On the outside we pasted the picture of a girl at the table saying thank you to God for her breakfast. And she had a glass of milk.

We set the basket in front of the pretty table. It was pretty today. There was a bowl of shiny apples and oranges and grapes on it. On one side of the bowl was the red Bible. It was open to the place that says, "We give thanks, O God, we give thanks." On the other side was the picture of the nursery children.

Everybody remembered to bring Thanksgiving money—I guess the mothers helped them remember 'cause they had the letters about it. Each one of us went up to the store and gave our money to Mommy, just like at a real store. Then Mommy handed us our powdered milk. We carried it over and put it in the basket.

But Mommy doesn't keep the money. Mrs. Gordon explained that. She has to take it and give it to the real store where she got the milk.

We finished our Thanksgiving-table cards. I had the most of anybody, 'cause so many people will be at our house for Thanksgiving dinner. And I didn't eat a single mint. Miss Cora helped us put our cards in our own sacks with our names on. I like for my name to be on things. I don't like to get somebody else's work.

It was such a happy day that we played a game about being at Sunday school. We marched around in a circle singing "Farmer in the Dell," only we didn't use those words. We sang, "We're glad that we are here, we're glad that we are here, heigh-ho the merrio, Kathy Ann's at church." I was in the middle. Then I chose Roger to be in the middle, and I went back to the circle. We kept on till everybody had a turn—even Mommy and Mrs. Gordon and Miss Cora! We had a good time.

Of course we sang our thank-you song for all good things to eat. We sang it right while we looked at our basket of powdered milk.

You know what, Thanksgiving day is in the Bible. There has been a Thanksgiving day a long, long, LONG time. The Bible people took the nicest things out of their gardens to church, and then they gave them to people who didn't have any.

Our story this morning was about the way they did it then. A little boy named Jesse went to church with his father and mother, and he carried his own basket. He had olives and grapes and figs and nuts in it. After church he took it to an old lady who was too old and tired to work in a garden any more. Jesse was one of God's helpers.

After the story Mrs. Gordon picked up the red Bible and said, "Here is something that Jesse and his old friend told God, and we still tell him today."

And we knew what it was without her reading it. We said, "We give thanks, O God, we give thanks."

Mrs. Gordon held the picture of the everyday-nursery children who will drink our powdered milk and grow strong. We'll be like Jesse in the thanksgiving of Bible days. But it's too far for all of us to go take the milk to the nursery, so we played that we did.

Gail and I and a few others were the nursery children. We sat down at a table. Mommy was the lady who takes care of the nursery.

She said, "It's lunch time. Would you like some milk?"

We said yes. Mommy pretended to look in the cupboard. She acted sad. "There isn't any milk. We can't have lunch."

Gail said, "I'm hungry."

And then Mrs. Gordon and the other children came over

to our table. They were carrying powdered milk. They gave it to us. We said thank you. Mommy said, "Now we can have our lunch."

We played like we were drinking milk, just the way the everyday-nursery children will drink it. We liked it.

It was Mommy who told God about it. "Thank you, God, for helpers who share their food with others."

That's what the nursery lady will say.

37 THAT'S WHY

Are Gail and I ever lucky that our mothers are the Sunday-school teachers! We got to go with them to take the powdered milk to the everyday nursery. We went in the car. Mommy didn't tell us till time to go, 'cause she was afraid maybe the road might get slippery and we couldn't drive.

Lowell went too. And Mommy said there would be room for Joyce and Chucky. But I didn't want to ask Joyce. I just wanted Gail.

Mommy talked to me. She said suppose Joyce's mother and Mrs. Gordon took Gail and Joyce to the city, wouldn't

I like to go with them? I guess I would. So I ran over and asked Joyce, and she was glad.

The nursery is in an ugly old place. The streets are ugly and the houses are ugly. I wouldn't like to live there. But the little boys and girls in the nursery were just like us. Maybe they don't like to live there either.

The lady thanked us for the powdered milk. And we stayed to see the children drink some of it! I felt glad.

Lowell played train with one of the little boys, and he didn't want to go home. He liked a boy whose face was real dark.

We had fun Thanksgiving. Grandmother Lowell says I've grown so big since she was here last summer. That's what big people always say. They're funny.

I had a hard time getting Mommy to set the Thanksgiving dinner table. She kept saying she had to stuff the turkey first and she had to fix the cranberries first and she had to make the rolls first.

I wanted the table set so I could put my cards to show everybody where to sit. Daddy helped me. I told everybody I made the cards. Keith wanted to eat his mint before dinner, but I wouldn't let him.

Before we sat down to the table, Daddy read a little piece out of our new red Bible. I didn't know all the words, but they sounded like a song and they made me feel nice. Then when we sat down to eat, Daddy asked me to say the prayer. I said, "We give thanks, O God, we give thanks."

This morning at Sunday school we told about Thanksgiving at our houses. Roger's Grandpa Block ate two mints —the one off his own card and the one off the grandma's.

Janet is still at my house, so she went to Sunday school. Mrs. Gordon let her help put up pictures. Janet liked the easel. We let her have a long turn painting pictures. We sang our "Friends" song 'cause she was a new friend. Of course she's my cousin. She liked visiting my Sunday school.

Gail and Chucky and Joyce and I all helped Mrs. Gordon tell the others about taking the powdered milk to the nursery.

Thanksgiving is nice, but Christmas is nicer. Christmas is the best time there is. I like to talk about Christmas a long time. We started talking about it this morning.

There was a little Christmas tree on the table. It didn't have any decorations on it. There was some colored paper on the table. I remembered about paper chains. We made some chains and put them on the tree. Another Sunday we'll hang more decorations on it.

When we sat on the rug, we set the tree on the floor in the middle. Mrs. Gordon sang about Christmas bells, jingle, jingle, jingle. Miss Cora made a sound just like the bells on the piano. We listened. Then we sang too.

Why do we have Christmas, Mrs. Gordon asked us. We said for Santa Claus to bring us presents. But she didn't talk about Santa Claus. She talked about Jesus. She showed us the picture of Jesus and the mothers and fathers and children who went to see him.

She didn't ask questions. But Waldo said, "That's Jesus." And Roger went up and touched Jesus.

We heard another story about Jesus being kind. One day he went to a friend's house to visit. The people heard he was there. A mother brought her sick baby. A man brought his friend who couldn't see. A woman who was not happy came. Jesus loved them all and helped them feel better. He told them—everybody who was standing around —God wants you to help one another.

Then we saw another picture of Jesus—when he was a third-grader—on a hill with flowers growing.

The last picture was Jesus when he was a little baby and his mommy was holding him.

Now I know. First Jesus was a baby just like Lowell and me. Then he grew till he was old enough to go to school. He grew and grew some more till he was a man and the children and the sick people went to see him.

Jesus had a birthday, just like I have. Only his wasn't the twenty-third of April. His was Christmas Day. That's why we have Christmas. Mrs. Gordon said so.

38 I FELT REAL QUIET

Guess who was back at Sunday school today. Hughy! He didn't like the other Sunday school where he went. His mother got mad.

But I didn't like for Hughy to be back very well. He was a bad boy. He bothered Mrs. Gordon telling a story. And it was a nice story. With real little toy people and a donkey and a sheep.

I saw the package right away. Mrs. Gordon said Joyce and I could open it. The little people and animals were inside. I knew who the baby was. Jesus. And his mother.

We helped Mrs. Gordon set them on the table. You call them a crèche. First there was hay like a real barn where animals live. And a manger is the box they eat out of—Mrs. Gordon told us. We put Jesus in the little manger and Mary and Joseph beside him. Then there were the men that took care of the sheeps. They're called shepherds.

I liked holding the little people. I was careful. I wouldn't drop Baby Jesus.

Now I want a crèche for our own house. Mommy said yes, we'll get one. I've talked about it all day. Daddy will buy one downtown tomorrow when he goes to work. I don't think it will be too big for him to carry home.

Our kindergarten room was full of Christmas today. There were different things to do at the tables. You could choose what you wanted. You could make a Christmas present for somebody. But you didn't have to. Mostly I played with the crèche. Then I played in the doll corner. I was Mother Mary, and I gave Baby Jesus a ride in the buggy. I fed him mashed beets.

You know what, Maribel's mother helped at the tables today. She is good at making things, just like Maribel. Judy is making something for her grandmother to put a ball of string in. Gail is fixing a calendar for her grandpa. Those of us who go to everyday kindergarten are making presents for our mothers and daddies there. So at Sunday school we can make them for other people.

The little ones like Roger are fixing bookmarks. Roger made one for his grandpa, and Miss Cora wrote on it for him. He showed it to me. He told everybody, "See what I made!"

Maybe I'll make something next Sunday.

I put more decorations on the little tree. Silver rain. Some of the children cut wreaths out of green paper. They pasted red paper berries on them. Mommy hung them at the windows.

Miss Cora played on the piano. I knew what it was. "Away in a Manger." Some of us big ones went over to the piano and sang.

Then we saw Mrs. Gordon sit down by the crèche. Pretty soon everybody was around her on the rug, and Kenneth asked if she would tell a story. She said yes—about the baby in the song asleep on the hay.

Mary and Joseph had to go on a long trip to write their names in the king's book. (That's when Hughy started to mess up things. He pushed a shepherd over. Mrs. Gordon took his hand off and looked at him hard.) Mary rode on a donkey and Joseph walked beside her. They got to Bethel-hem and tried to find a place to stay all night. (Hughy stuck the donkey on Joseph's back.)

Mrs. Gordon said that she was sorry Hughy didn't want to hear the story and that if he went out in the hall, he wouldn't have to listen. So Mommy took him out and stayed with him. Hughy didn't like that.

But the rest of us were glad he was gone. We wanted to hear the story.

There wasn't any room for Mary and Joseph in the motel, so they had to go sleep back in the barn with the animals. That night little Baby Jesus was born. Mary laid him in the manger. Mary and Joseph were happy.

The shepherds were out on the hill taking care of their sheeps. They heard about the baby in Bethel-hem. They wanted to see him. So they hurried to the barn. They thought he was a wonderful baby. Mary sang him to sleep. And that was the first Christmas night.

I felt real quiet when Mrs. Gordon bowed her head and said, "Thank you, God, for Jesus and for his birthday and Christmas."

She gave us green paper Christmas trees with a letter on them to take home. Mommy read me what it says. It tells the mothers and daddies what we're doing at Sunday school for Christmas, and they can come visit us the Sunday before Christmas. And it tells about the Christmas party.

Bruce cried this morning. He fell down the stairs coming to our room. Mommy said little children's rooms shouldn't be in the basement. Maybe when we have a new church, the kindergarten room will be up on the ground. When Daddy goes to his committee, he looks at pictures of new churches with lots of Sunday-school rooms. But **Mr. Block** doesn't like them.

39 WHAT PRESENTS TELL

Our house is like Christmas now, too. We have the crèche. Guess where it is. In the fireplace. It's like the cave where the barn was that Jesus was born in. My daddy fixed it the best of anybody's crèche. When we get our Christmas tree, we'll put it in front and turn a light on the crèche.

Today I felt like working on presents at Sunday school. I helped make dustrags for Mr. Mac! Pretty red and green ones. Maribel's mother showed us how. We took turns pushing the needle in and out, in and out, all around the edge.

We fixed a blotter for Dr. Hart's desk. We pasted pictures and Christmas seals around the outside. Judy mustn't tell him. It's a surprise.

Surprises are fun. Some of the children had bookmarks and calendars ready to wrap. Mrs. Gordon walked around and said, "Let us love one another."

That's what presents tell people—that you love them. When I was little, I thought you gave Christmas presents to Jesus. Now I know. We make people happy on Jesus' birthday by doing what he wanted us to do.

We made a calendar for Mr. Broshaw, too. He's coming to visit us next Sunday.

Just as we finished our presents, I heard a surprise. A record player! Waldo's mother let us borrow theirs. We sat on the rug to listen. All the teachers listened. I liked "Little Town of Bethel-hem." But I liked "Silent Night" the best of all. We were real quiet when Waldo played it. I felt like I was in the music.

I was all ready for Mrs. Gordon to say, "Dear God, we're glad for beautiful music that tells us about Jesus and Christmas."

She opened the red Bible and read, "Let us love one another." That's why Jesus was born—to help us be kind to people. We helped Mrs. Gordon tell the story about Baby Jesus again. When she held the little people up, we told about them.

Hughy started to grab Baby Jesus out of the manger. Mrs. Gordon took his hand and said, "Hughy," the way mothers do when they really mean it. And you know what, he quit! I guess he didn't want to go out in the hall again.

Mrs. Gordon added some more to the story. About the wise men. They saw a bright star in the sky and they knew Baby Jesus was born. They rode on camels to see him. They didn't get there in time, but they found him later. They gave him presents.

We added the wise men to the crèche today. But we didn't set them clear inside. We set them a little bit outside. Then we put a blue paper with a shiny star on it back of the crèche. That was the star the wise men saw in the blue sky.

That's why we have a star on top of Christmas trees.

Mrs. Gordon asked would we like to cut down our own Christmas tree and decorate it. We said we would. She said all right, we'd take our little hatchets and find a nice, strong tree and cut it down and put a star at the top.

I thought that would be fun. We all ran to get our coats. The teachers stopped us. Mrs. Gordon didn't mean really to go outside and get a real tree. She meant to pretend. She just made a mistake. It was her fault. She said so. Teachers and mothers make mistakes sometimes.

So we pretended. Chucky and Hughy were trees—Hughy liked being one. We cut them down and tied ropes around

them. Then we brought them home, and they held their arms out and we played putting decorations on them.

We talked about our mothers and fathers visiting us next Sunday. We'll sing our Christmas songs and tell them about Baby Jesus. We'll give presents to Mr. Mac and Dr. Hart and Mr. Broshaw.

Daddy doesn't want to go to the Christmas party next Friday. He's afraid it will be like the one last Christmas. But Mommy says it won't. Mrs. Hart is fixing it nice.

Daddy is taking a nap. When he gets up, we're going to put a blue sky and a bright star up in the top of our fireplace over our crèche. And our wise men were too close to the manger. I moved them farther away.

40 SHARING CHRISTMAS

I have so many things to tell.

Daddy was wrong. The party was fun. He liked it. There wasn't room for all the Sunday school at one time. The ones with little children went first, and after us the big children and their mothers and fathers. We got home in time to go to bed early.

We took toys. But this time they were for children who don't go to our Sunday school. They were for the children who live around the big building where the everyday nursery is. They don't have many toys. Lowell and I went to the store with Mommy and picked out a ball and a woolly dog that looks like Y'honor.

We took clothes, too. I gave one of my dresses that I like myself. I helped Mommy wash it nice and clean, and she ironed it. I hope some little girl likes it.

We wrapped the toys and clothes in white paper. At church we put them under the big Christmas tree.

We played games—even the daddies played. Mrs. Hart wouldn't let them sit down. Mr. Broshaw helped. He laughed a lot. I liked the game where you put a rag over your eyes and pinned a present on a paper Christmas tree. I did better than Daddy!

We had re-freshments, too. Red juice—you call it punch —in paper cups, and cookies. I ate a Santa Claus with chocolate buttons.

All of us—even the daddies—sang Christmas songs. Then Mr. Broshaw told us the surprise. He said, "Listen." We did. Mrs. Terry started playing the organ upstairs. We could all go upstairs to the big room.

It never looked that way before. A little bit dark. There were candles burning at the windows and big pieces of Christmas trees tied with red ribbon up in front.

It made you feel glad and quiet. Even Lowell didn't talk.

Then there were pictures. Not the fast-moving kind. The slow kind. In pretty colors. The whole Christmas story.

Dr. Hart read out of the Bible with each picture—about

98

Mary and Joseph and Baby Jesus and the shepherds and the wise men. I liked it.

At the end the organ played "Silent Night," and we walked out real quiet.

Mommy and Mrs. Gordon went over to church yesterday to get things ready for Sunday school. When we got there this morning, Miss Cora had name tags for the mothers and fathers who were visiting and for us, too, so they could tell who we were.

Mrs. Gordon stood at the door and shook hands. Then we showed the mothers and fathers the things in our room. I led Daddy to the crèche and to the paper chains I made.

After we showed the presents for Mr. Mac and Mr. Broshaw and Dr. Hart, Maribel's mother and Miss Cora helped us wrap them up.

The mothers sat on our little chairs. Some of the daddies stood up. Mrs. Gordon told them she'd like to have a bench under the windows for people to sit on and for us to stand on and look outdoors.

We sat on the rug just like every other Sunday. But we didn't have as much room. Mrs. Gordon asked how could we share the story of Christmas with our mothers and fathers. Joyce said sing. So we sang all our Christmas songs.

You can read the story too. In the Bible. Mrs. Gordon read it in the red Bible. Hughy said tell it with the little people. So we looked at the crèche and talked about Mary and Joseph and Baby Jesus and the others. Roger took the little sheep to show his mother.

Next we played the story. Donna went over to the doll corner and got a doll. Mrs. Gordon wrapped a white cloth all around the doll from the toes clear up to the head. That's the way mothers wrapped their babies when Jesus was little.

There was a blue cloth for Mary to put over her head and a brown cloth for Joseph. Chucky thought of a manger.

99

We set two little chairs together and put a doll blanket on them.

Donna was Mary and Jay was Joseph. Mrs. Gordon asked us what Mary and Joseph would do, and we thought they'd be looking at the baby and putting him to sleep.

So Donna laid the doll on the chairs and she patted it, and Jay watched. The rest of us were shepherds. We tiptoed up to look at the baby while Miss Cora played "Away in a Manger."

We were the story ourselves!

Then Mrs. Gordon said, "Let us love one another," and we knew what way that is of telling about Christmas. Giving presents.

She and the other teachers had a Christmas surprise for us to keep in our room every Sunday. We shut our eyes and waited till she said open them. It's a new picture book, about when Jesus was a little boy. Mrs. Gordon turned through it for us to see.

We could hardly wait to give our presents to Mr. Mac and Mr. Broshaw and Dr. Hart. They opened them and looked at them and said thank you.

Then Mr. Broshaw said there was a surprise for us out in the hall. He and Mr. Mac went out to get it. There wasn't room to push it clear in, but we could see it. It's the coat rack Mr. Mac made for us. It's finished! Now we'll have a good place to hang our wraps out in the hall. We all said, "Thank you, Mr. Mac."

The bright star tells us about Christmas, so the teachers gave each one of us and the visitors a star cookie to eat.

Mrs. Gordon said, "We've had a happy time today, haven't we?"

And Roger said, "Tell God."

We did. "Thank you, God, for a happy day and for Christmas and for mothers and fathers."

100

41 SO SURPRISED

It isn't Sunday yet, but I can't wait to tell some things. Yesterday Mommy took Lowell and me downtown to see Santa Claus. Daddy met us, and we had dinner in the res-taurant. That's something I like to do every Christmas.

I asked Santa Claus for a walking doll. I told him we liked the doggie he brought us last Christmas. Lowell asked for a filling station with cars. I know something else he's going to get. I bought it for him with Mommy when he wasn't looking. It's a soap rabbit to take a bath with.

So now I'm playing Santa Claus. I've hidden Mommy's and Daddy's presents that I made at kindergarten, too. They try to guess, but they can't.

This morning when we were standing in line with our groceries, we saw Donna's mother. She liked visiting Sunday school and seeing Donna play Mary. She isn't mad about Bushy Squirrel any more, 'cause Donna does know about God.

One day she asked Donna why do we have thanks at the dinner table, and Donna said it's a part of God's plan for us to thank him. Donna's mother was so surprised!

Mommy was happy another time today. She got a Christmas card from Mr. Broshaw. He wrote on it, "Thank you for what you are doing in the kindergarten."

Our tree goes clear to the ceiling and has pretty lights on it, and there's a light on the crèche in the fireplace. Everybody who comes to our house says, "How nice!" Every night Mommy plays the piano and we all sing Christmas songs, even Daddy. It's fun.

On Christmas Day we're going to have company for dinner. His name is Mr. Inan. He's from a place 'way, 'way off, named Turkey. Isn't that funny! He's from Turkey and he'll eat turkey. He goes to college in the city.

Dr. Hart asked Mommy if Mr. Inan could come to dinner. Some other people in Rose Park will have company like him too. When Mommy and Daddy were little like me, they didn't get to have somebody for dinner from 'way far off.

Lowell and I already have our stockings hanging up at the fireplace. There's one for Y'honor, too.

I can hardly wait. I wonder what I'll take to Sunday school Sunday. Mrs. Gordon said we could bring one of our Christmas presents to show.

42) SHE LET US CHOOSE

I got the walking doll. I named her Ann, 'cause she's my little girl. Lowell got his filling station. We got other things, too. Daddy took pictures of us opening our packages. He gave the whole family a present—a globe— that's the world.

I watched him and Mommy open their presents from me. Were they ever surprised! I made them at everyday kindergarten—a thing to set hot dishes on for Mommy and my handprint on a paperweight for Daddy.

Mommy put the hot pad under the gravy bowl at dinner. Mr. Inan liked the gravy. And he liked the turkey—he laughed and said he was eating himself. He didn't know about cranberries. And he didn't know about the crèche. I told him all about Mary and Joseph and the Baby Jesus.

He played filling station with Lowell. He liked Y'honor and Y'honor liked him. Most of the time he and Daddy talked big words. We took him riding past our church.

He showed us a picture of his church in Turkey. It isn't

102

like our church. It has a round top. We lighted our globe, and he put his finger on the place where he lives.

I'm glad Mr. Inan came to our house for Christmas. When Mommy was little, she was scared of people in Turkey. But I'm not scared of Mr. Inan.

I took Ann to Sunday school this morning. I let Judy play with Ann, and I played with her doll. But I didn't let everybody play with her, for I didn't want anything to happen to her. Mommy said that was all right.

Hughy took Chucky's boat and pushed it around the rug. He yelled, "Bang, bang, I'm a gunboat! You're dead!"

Mrs. Gordon said, "I know another kind of boat. Let me have a turn." She pushed the boat and said, "I'm a food boat. I'm carrying food to hungry children."

Chucky was a fishing boat. He was catching fish for people to eat.

Roger was a package boat taking a package to his daddy.

I was a riding boat going to Turkey.

Mrs. Gordon showed us one of her presents, too. A bottle of perfume. She pulled the top off and let us each one smell.

She read us a story out of Maribel's new Christmas book. Then she let us choose the songs we wanted to sing and the stories we wanted to hear again.

She knew we were kind of tired from Christmas, so we didn't do much work. But we did draw pictures. She asked us to shut our eyes and think real hard of all the things we liked about Christmas. It was funny—I could see things even with my eyes closed. That's a good way to think. Then each of us drew a picture of what we liked best about Christmas.

I drew our fireplace with the light shining on Baby Jesus.

When we were through, all of us told about our pictures. Some were Christmas trees and some were Santa Claus and some were presents.

When I ex-plained about mine, Mrs. Gordon put her arm around me and loved me. I felt like I was in a different town.

She asked us how many had read all of the book that we took home to keep a long time ago. If we haven't, we'd better do it right away, 'cause next Sunday we get a new book!

We used our new coat rack today. We set our boots on the shelf at the bottom. Mrs. Gordon asked us please all to put our names inside our wraps and boots.

When it was time to go home, we didn't all run out into the hall at one time. Mrs. Gordon said, "All the people who have something red on may get their wraps." They brought their wraps in, and another color went out—and another color—till we were all used up.

Hughy tried to slip out the door before it was time, but Miss Cora was watching and stopped him. She laughed and said, "Nobody leaves till we're all ready."

As we started home with our pictures, Mrs. Gordon whispered in each one's ear. This is what she said: "Happy New Year."

43 SNOW LIKE WOOL

The teachers had a meeting at our house the other day. They talked about our new books and taking the magazines to the mothers and what to do at Sunday school every Sunday. Maribel's mother will be a helper all the time. Mommy said that was the most im-portant thing—to have enough helpers.

She sent me over to Maribel's house with a book for her mother to read about teaching Sunday school.

Today we got our new books. And are they ever pretty! I like colored pictures in books. This one is about all the sur-prises Jacky finds outdoors.

Mrs. Gordon opened the book to a thank-you prayer. It was a poem. Sometimes I like to feel a poem. She said it for us. Then we did it with her three times. We learned it well enough so that after our story we did it again. It was nice saying something all together like big people. We can say it at home, too.

We heard the first story in our new book. Jacky woke up one morning and there was snow on the ground. He was surprised, 'cause there wasn't any snow when he went to bed. He ate breakfast real fast so he could go out and make a snow man and play with his sled. He thought snow was just fun. But Jacky's mother told him snow was for something else, too.

It covers up the little seeds sleeping in the ground and keeps them warm. When it melts into water, it goes into the ground to help the seeds grow.

Jacky asked his mother who sent the snow. Mrs. Gordon didn't have to tell us. We knew. God. Jacky's mother found the verse in the Bible about snow. Mrs. Gordon found it too. She read it to us:

"He gives snow like wool."

Wool *does* look like snow. Mrs. Gordon had some real wool off of a sheep's back. She put it in our treasure box. It keeps the sheep warm in wintertime. In the summertime you cut it off and make it into cloth for clothes. That's the way God planned. My snow suit is made out of wool.

You know what, even doggies have heavier coats in winter than in summer. Mrs. Gordon told us to look. I did. Y'honor's hair is sort of bunchy now. God just thought about everything.

Sometimes in winter children are sick with a cold or measles and can't come to Sunday school. Mrs. Gordon said she doesn't want you to come to church when you're sick.

Today we made puzzles to send to sick children. We pasted big pictures on cardboard to cut into pieces. Miss Cora put the pieces of each puzzle in an envelope. If I get sick, I want the one of the girl riding a two-wheeler. I hope I get a two-wheeler for my birthday.

Roger had a birthday today. Is it ever fun to have a birthday now! Roger's mother painted a great big pink and blue cake on cardboard. It's in three layers. Around the edge of the layers Miss Cora wrote all our names. When you have a birthday, you paste a little white candle above where your name is. It hangs on the wall, and we can find our own names.

Then there's a new piggy bank for birthday pennies. It's like a real pig. Mrs. Gordon told us the story. Once a boy raised a pig and sold it and gave the money to a missionary to buy medicine for sick people. So now we put our money in Pete the Pig, and when he's full, we'll send it to buy medicine for boys and girls who are sick with lep-ro-sy.

Today Mrs. Gordon read us a letter from the boys and girls we sent Christmas presents to. They liked the toys and clothes. They pasted pictures on their letter. I like to get letters.

Guess what, while we were at Sunday school, it began to snow. Great big fluffy snowflakes. We could hardly see it out of our high windows. But Mrs. Gordon let us put on our wraps a little bit early and go outside.

We ran and let the snow fall on our faces and had fun. Then she had a surprise for us—a glass that makes things look big. She let every one of us look at the snow that fell on our arms. And you know what, every little snowflake has a lot of points like a star. . . . God made it beautiful.

We all stood together and said, "Thank you, God, for giving us snow."

44 GOD'S LAWS

Guess who was our teacher this morning. Mommy! Guess who told a story. Miss Cora! Mrs. Gordon went to visit another Sunday school today.

Mommy studied hard. She let me help her decide some of the things to do. She told Daddy lots of people could learn to be a good teacher by paying attention to the teacher's book. It tells so many things you can do.

Mommy wrote everything we might do this morning on a piece of paper. She took it to Sunday school and kept it with her.

We're fixing a day-night thing to go around the wall. It's a long strip of white paper with a big black mark in the middle. One side is for day and one is for night. Miss Cora wrote a Bible verse on top, "God made day and night." Then we cut out pictures and pasted them on the side they belonged on. Mostly I found daytime pictures—children at school and a man feeding his chickens and the sun shining. Joan and Judy found some nighttime ones—the stars and a boy in bed and people eating supper.

Maribel didn't cut out pictures. She drew a girl and a boy making a snow man. Mommy told her we couldn't get along without her good pictures. Maribel smiled.

God made the daytime for us to work and play and the nighttime for us to rest. He gave us the sun in the daytime and the moon and stars at night. I wonder how he thought of so many things. I asked Daddy why does morning always come after night, and he said it's a law. Mommy heard him and said not one of his lawyer laws but one of God's laws.

You just don't have to worry. God fixed things up and they keep on going. Daddy is reading a book so he can answer my questions about God better. But nobody knows everything about God.

Mommy guessed other children would like to know about God's laws too. This morning at Sunday school she talked about the sun and the moon and the stars and the morning always coming.

They tell us God loves us.

Some people are good like God. That's the way the shepherd was who took care of one hundred sheeps. Miss Cora told us about him. One night he called his sheeps to come home and go to bed. He counted them one, two, three, four—clear on up to one hunderd. Only there wasn't one hundred. He got to ninety-nine—and that was all. One poor little sheep was gone!

The shepherd left the other sheeps and went out and looked for the one that was lost. He walked all over the hills calling. He looked in holes and behind bushes. Just when he was almost ready to give up, he heard ba-a-a, ba-a-a. The little sheep had fallen into a deep hole. The shepherd took him home and rubbed medicine on him and oh, he was so happy 'cause he had found his lost sheep.

108

When Miss Cora told the story, I felt like I was going right along with the shepherd. I'd go look for Y'honor that way if he was lost.

After we got home, Mommy asked me, "Kathy Ann, did you know that story was in the Bible?" and I said no. Mommy said oh, my, she forgot to tell us that it's a story Jesus told. She was mad at herself for not remembering.

We began learning a new song at Sunday school this morning. When Mommy felt bad about the Bible story, I told her anyway she can sing better than Mrs. Gordon. She and I can sing the new song together. I like it. It says:

> It is a good thing to give thanks
> So we have a prayer to say,
> Thank you, God, for all good things
> Each night and every day.[1]

I know the "good things" God gives us—flowers and sunshine and stars and moon and snowflakes.

You know what, everybody in our whole Sunday school now has something new! Envelopes to carry our offering to church in every Sunday. I keep my envelopes on the shelf with my other Sunday-school things so I don't forget. Now our offering can't roll around on the floor at Sunday school.

We had a whole basket full of envelopes this morning. Mommy talked about it and then she said to God, "Dear God, thank you for this money. Thank you for the good things it will buy for our church and for others."

Yesterday when Mommy went to the church to get our room ready for Sunday school, Lowell and I went too. We walked clear upstairs to the big room. I've been wanting to see that organ Mrs. Terry plays. Lowell and I climbed up to it, and I tried to play it.

[1] From *Learning in the Church Kindergarten*, Part VI, p. 126. Used by permission.

Mr. Mac just all-of-a-sudden came from somewhere. He said, "You children can't be up here."

I said, "Oh, yes, I can. I'm one of the owners of this church."

But we got down.

45 HE NEVER WANTS TO MISS

I *did* get the puzzle of the girl riding a two-wheeler. The Sunday-school children sent it to me through the mail.

I'm sick. First I had the measles. Then I had an infection. I can't go to Sunday school, but they didn't forget me, 'cause they sent me the puzzle. After I worked it once, then I could work it real fast. Mommy keeps cutting it into more pieces.

I can't talk about Sunday school. It makes Lowell cry. He can't go either 'cause he has the measles. But he loves Mrs. Hart, and he never wants to miss the nursery department a single time.

Last Sunday Mommy forgot and had our special Sunday dinner—chicken and ice cream. When Lowell saw the chicken, he yelled and yelled—"It's Sunday! Why didn't I go to Sunday school?"

Mommy had to hold him on her lap and talk to him before he would quit crying. I got hungry waiting.

Mommy said to Daddy, "Oh, my, Lowell doesn't need to win a prize pin to go to Sunday school every Sunday. He just wants to go because he likes what he does there."

Daddy reads to us almost every night. Some nights he has to go to that committee to build a new church. Mr. Block still wants the colored windows.

110

46 WE HELPED DORCAS

Mommy went to Sunday school early this morning. Daddy took Lowell and me. I could hardly wait to get there, 'cause I missed such a long time.

I didn't even wait to take off my wraps. I knocked on the door and pushed it wide open and said real loud, "I'm back!"

Everybody was glad. Mrs. Gordon let me put water on the bulb. That's something I missed. The others have been watching it every Sunday. It will be a flower for Easter.

If you miss Sunday school, you don't know about things when you go back. You ought to be there every time except when you're sick.

The treasure box had new treasures in it. Pussy willows and new little leaves and a bird's nest. Just like Jacky in our storybook found. They say, "Wake up, wake up, it's spring."

Mommy read my Sunday-school book to me even when I couldn't go to Sunday school.

Miss Cora took the winter pictures down. Now we have spring pictures. You know what, the Bible tells about spring. It says winter is over and birds and flowers are here. Every time Mrs. Gordon read a little bit of those verses, one of us chose a picture that showed it.

At Easter time you get new clothes. I'm going to have a new dress for Easter-and-birthday. Today Mrs. Gordon told us a story about a Bible lady named Dorcas. She liked to help people the way Jesus did. Some of the children in her town needed warm clothes. Dorcas was a good sew-er. She got some cloth and made a dress for a little girl.

We helped her make it. When Mrs. Gordon came to that part of the story, we all played that we were cutting out the dress—snip, snip, snip. Then we held up our needles and pushed the thread through. Maribel remembered something that the teacher forgot. You have to tie the thread on!

Then we went in and out, in and out, till the dress was made.

Next we helped Dorcas make a coat for the girl's brother. We wrapped the dress and the coat in a package and took them to the children's home. They were so happy that they tried them on right away. The mother said to Dorcas, "You are really one of Jesus' helpers."

We liked that story. There was more to it. Some of the ladies in our church sew too. Right in our very kindergarten room—not on Sunday, on another day. Joan's mother is one of them. They sew things for babies and children in the county hospital. Some of the children are sick and have to stay there a long time. I know about being sick. I wouldn't like to stay in a hospital for a long, long time.

Mrs. Gordon opened a big box. We all watched. Inside were the things the ladies sewed. Mrs. Gordon passed them around. Each one of us got to touch them. The cute little bootees for a new baby. The bag to hold toys that you hang on a bed. And the quilt, with colors in it just like our clothes—green like the dress I had on today and pink like Joyce's dress. Hughy bet the quilt took a hundred stitches, and Mrs. Gordon said even more than a hundred.

She asked us what more do gifts need that you send to somebody. We knew. You write a card. Mrs. Gordon wondered if we could help the ladies by writing the cards. We said yes. We went to the tables and Miss Cora and Maribel's mother had the paper and crayons ready for us.

Joan drew her baby brother. He wears bootees too. I don't have a baby brother, so I drew flowers. The teachers showed us how to write "LOVE" along with our names. While we were working, Mrs. Gordon walked around and said, "Even little children are known by what they do." I guessed—that's a Bible verse. We did it.

The reason Mommy went to church early this morning was to get ready for the meeting. It was at three o'clock. The fathers and mothers were invited. And this time there was something to eat—tea and coffee and cookies.

Mommy and Daddy have just got home from the meeting. Mr. and Mrs. Gordon are here too. There's lots of talking. Mommy and Mrs. Gordon think there should have been more mothers and fathers to drink the coffee. But Daddy and Mr. Gordon tell them to be glad more came than last time. And to be glad Maribel's mother stood up and told the others it's a good kindergarten. And to be glad some of the people asked questions about Easter and the Bible. Dr. Hart helped answer the questions.

Maybe there will be a mothers' club. A club is like a committee—to go to.

47 HAPPY EASTER

My new Easter dress wasn't nearly so nice as the new girl's. Hers was silk. And stuck out. She had a hat with ribbon hanging down under her chin. She had white gloves and she kept them on all during Sunday school. I showed her the easel, but she wouldn't paint, 'cause she didn't want to get anything on her dress.

Her name was Marla. Her mother brought her early just when Mommy and I got there. Her mother had on silky clothes too. They just moved to Rose Park, and she thinks every child should go to Sunday school and be with other children. She said, "Now, Marla, you do what the teacher tells you."

Our bulb has turned into a white flower for Easter. Mrs. Gordon set it on the little table with the Bible. She asked what song it made us think of. We knew. It's one of the "good things" we thank God for. Of course I helped God by watering it.

We talked about our new clothes. We should say thank you to our mothers and fathers for buying them. We like to have new dresses and coats in the springtime just the way the trees get new leaves. They make us feel new and happy.

And Easter is a happy time. We think about Jesus the same as we do at Christmas. Jay said he saw on television that Jesus got killed. Mrs. Gordon explained: There were some people who didn't understand the things Jesus told them, and they made him die. But his love kept right on living, and it's still living today.

We looked at pictures and talked about all the stories we remembered of Jesus being kind to people.

Mrs. Gordon wondered what should we do with our Easter flower. Maybe there was somebody who couldn't go to church who would like to see it. Waldo knew somebody. A grandma who lives next door to him and can't walk very well. He calls her Grandma Janson even though she isn't his real grandma. His mother gives her flowers out of their garden in summertime.

We all said Waldo could take our flower to Grandma Janson.

The big children didn't have Sunday school today, 'cause there was church two times. But Mrs. Gordon and Mommy both thought we kindergartners should have our own Sunday school in our own room.

When Marla's mother came in after Sunday school, Mrs. Gordon talked to her and gave her something to take home to read.

Now that Easter is here, pretty soon it's my birthday. I think I'll get the two-wheeler. Daddy can't stand hearing me talk about it much longer.

It's 'cause we're paying for our house that we haven't much money. Daddy didn't think I needed a two-wheeler till I was older. But other children have them when they're six.

God likes to have us tell him things, so I told him about the bicycle. I was ready for bed and Mommy was going to PTA and I didn't think she'd hear me. I prayed, "Dear God, please send Daddy some more money so he can get me a two-wheeler."

But Mommy did hear. She took off her coat and she called Daddy, and we talked. Mommy said, "Kathy Ann, you know God doesn't drop money down for people." I did know. I didn't hear him say yes.

Mommy said I could ask him to help me grow strong and careful for a two-wheeler. But Daddy has to pay the money.

Then I remembered. I have some money too. In the bank. That my grandfathers and Aunt Sue and Uncle Dick gave me. I could help pay for the two-wheeler myself. Mommy and Daddy kissed me and tucked me in bed and said they'd think about it. I'm glad God gave me such a nice mother and father.

You know what, I think God made mothers and fathers and teachers for helpers.

GOD CAN UNDERSTAND BOTH

48

I got the two-wheeler! Partly with my own money. Daddy says I own the training wheel at least. I have to leave the training wheel on till I'm seven years old.

Joyce doesn't have a two-wheeler yet. She watched me ride and ride, and you know what, I wished she had a bicycle too. I let her ride mine. Mommy put her arm around me. She said, "Kathy Ann, you're growing up."

I felt a little bit good like God.

Mrs. Gordon sent me a birthday card in the mail. No other teacher ever sent me a card. I like to get mail.

At Sunday school today I pasted the white candle above my name on the cake. Everybody counted when I dropped my pennies in Pete the Pig for the sick children. The best thing was when Mrs. Gordon told God my name—"Dear God, we are glad for Kathy Ann. Help her to grow strong and good."

I am growing big enough to do more jobs at home. Now that I'm six, I make my own bed every morning.

Marla liked Pete the Pig. She took off her white gloves today.

Waldo brought a letter from Grandma Janson. She said thank you for the flower we sent. She looks at it every day.

Now that I'm six, I have an allowance—twenty-five cents every week. It's my own money. I put two nickels of it in my Sunday-school envelope as soon as I got it. It's a good thing I did, 'cause I lost the rest of it. I had it in my pocket to show people, and I guess it rolled out when I fell over on my bike. But Daddy won't give me any more till next Saturday. I won't take it out to show any more.

There was something besides my birthday at Sunday school. A missionary! Mrs. Ray. She lives at that mission station in Japan. She's here for a visit. Mr. Ray is here too. He talked to the grownups, and Mrs. Ray came to see us. I liked her. She had on a dress like the ladies in Japan wear.

She said she was a missionary like Paul. I told her my daddy's name is Paul. She was glad to know it. In our red Bible she pointed to "Paul." The Paul-in-the-Bible was the first missionary. He went everywhere telling people about Jesus.

Mrs. Ray tells the boys and girls in Japan about Jesus. She showed us the picture of one of the big boys in her school. His name is Fumio. He wants to be a preacher, but he doesn't have enough money to go to college. He doesn't have any father or mother. He's good to the little boys and girls. He tells them stories. You know what story they like best? About the children who went to see Jesus.

The Japanese girls have pretty dresses for special days. Mrs. Ray tried one of them on Joan.

We sang our "Friends" song for Mrs. Ray. Then she said a prayer in the words that the children in Japan use. We couldn't tell what they were, so she told us in our own words. But it doesn't make any difference to God. He can understand both ways.

Guess what Mrs. Ray gave us for our room. A picture that the children in her school painted. It's flowers and birds— better than we can draw. We chose the place on the wall for Miss Cora to put it.

Maybe we can send something to their school. Maybe we can send some money to Fumio so he can go to college.

Mommy had our globe at Sunday school, and the children liked turning the light on inside. Mrs. Ray put her finger on Japan.

And you know what, next Sunday a real little boy from Japan is coming to our Sunday school! His name is Kuizo. His mother and daddy came over here to go to college. We'll play with him and sing our songs for him.

49 PEOPLE HAVE LAWS

We had fun with Kuizo. He has black hair and his eyes and nose aren't exactly like mine, but he likes to build with blocks. Everybody wanted to play with him at the same time, so we had to take turns. Even Marla played to- day. She had on a dress that wasn't silk.

Kuizo knows our words, so we could talk to him. Mrs. Gordon asked him if he knew any Sunday-school songs, and he said, "Jesus Loves Me." We all sang it together. We haven't sung it for a long time. I felt glad to hear it again. We want Kuizo to come back another time.

His mother and daddy talked to the big children. His daddy is learning to be a preacher like Dr. Hart.

So now we're going to help Fumio, the other boy over in Japan, go to college and be a preacher too. The one Mrs. Ray told us about. We all have a little picture of him. It's pasted on the front of a thing you put dimes in. Everybody in Sunday school will bring dimes to church on Children's Day. Mommy and Daddy and I are all filling our dime holders together.

Now I know—all the people in the whole world are God's

118

children. He loves them. Mommy thinks he even loves Mrs. Spencer.

Mrs. Spencer did do it the other day. Call the police. Y'honor scratched one of her tomato plants. The policeman told Daddy that there's a new law that dogs shouldn't run around by themselves.

We'll simply have to take Y'honor around on a leash. He doesn't like it. Other dogs run around. But Daddy says we should o-bey the law. God has laws and people have laws. He started to tell me how we get laws, but I didn't want to listen that much.

Mommy said if we had a garden, we wouldn't like it for some dog to come in and dig holes. Mrs. Spencer doesn't have any little children or any dog, and Mommy thinks maybe she is lonely. And maybe she has a headache.

Yesterday Mommy made rolls, and she gave me some to take to Mrs. Spencer. I was a little bit scared. But when

119

she came to the door, she looked surprised. She said, "Thank you, Kathy Ann. I'll eat these for supper."

Maybe Daddy will build a fence around the back yard for Y'honor.

He and Mommy were talking about Kuizo and Mrs. Spencer, and Mommy said she had learned a lot being a Sunday-school teacher. Isn't that funny?

She and the other teachers have a training school again. It's at night. Maribel's mother goes. Mr. Broshaw goes too.

50 THREE ROGERS

This was Children's Day. But we didn't stay up-stairs the whole time. I wasn't a hollyhock. All of us were just children. Nobody said a speech. We all went up in front and sang some of our regular songs like any Sunday. We wanted our mothers and fathers and the big children to like our songs the same way we do. Nobody clapped hands, but I saw Daddy and we smiled at each other.

Then we put our dime holders between a big Bible and the lighted globe that is really ours (we just let the church use it). Everybody in the whole church gave dimes. There's enough money for Fumio to go to college in Japan for a whole year.

When we went downstairs to our own room, we walked real quiet like kitty cats, so we wouldn't dis-turb the people upstairs. We had visitors. Guess who. Roger's daddy—Roger Block, Junior—is home. You know what, he's been to the very place where Fumio lives. He told us.

And when he was our size, he went to Sunday school in the same room we have.

Roger's grandpa came to see us too. All three Rogers. A granddaddy and a daddy and a little boy, all at one time, in our kindergarten. Mrs. Gordon thought we should have a picture of them.

Roger's daddy said he had a fast camera in his car. And would we like to have a whole kindergarten picture taken of us in our Children's Day clothes?

We went out in the yard and he took our pictures— and just like that, he showed it to us! He'll give every one of us a picture.

Then Mommy took a picture of the three Rogers. Now she's writing a story about them all being at our kindergarten, and she'll take it and the picture to the *Rose Leaf*.

Roger showed his daddy and his granddaddy the pictures on the wall in our room and the treasure box and the red Bible. They listened while we sang and talked and told stories about the pictures. We sang our "Friends" song.

And you know what, Mrs. Gordon has a birthday. She put her birthday pennies in Pete the Pig just like us! We sang "Happy Birthday" to her. Hughy said, "You didn't paste your candle on the cake." So she did.

The three Rogers waited till everybody had gone except Mrs. Gordon and Mommy and Gail and me. The daddy Roger wanted to say thank you for making little Roger so happy while he was away. When he was a little boy, the kindergarten room didn't look nice like it does now. He used to cry and not want to come to Sunday school. Now he wants good Sunday schools all over the world.

The grandpa didn't talk much.

51 "BE NOT AFRAID"

The picture of the three Rogers was in the newspaper with the story Mommy wrote. Grandpa Roger called

Mommy and said thank you. He wants six copies to send to people.

Something really happened today. It was dark in our kindergarten room, so we had the lights on. All-of-a-sudden, while we were singing, the lights went out. There was big thunder. It was almost like night. Rain came down hard.

I didn't like it very well. Bruce began to cry. I went to sit by Mommy.

Mrs. Gordon put her arms around Bruce. She said if he would quit crying so he could listen, she'd tell us a story. Bruce didn't quit crying. Mommy took him over into the corner to talk to him.

Mrs. Gordon told us about thunder. It's a part of God's world. It comes with rain sometimes, first lightning, then thunder. The lightning is e-lec-tricity just like in the light bulb. You have to be careful, 'cause sometimes lightning hurts people. It's safe inside our church. God loves us even when there's lightning. Thunder makes a big boom boom, but it won't hurt you. After a while the sun shines again. Mrs. Gordon held the red Bible and told us a verse in it— "Be not afraid."

It was a good time to sing our pitter-patter song. Then we said thank you to God for sending the rain for the gardens.

When Bruce's mother came after him, she said she is scared of thunder too. Mrs. Gordon talked to her.

It's still raining. I don't want it to rain any more, 'cause if it doesn't rain tomorrow, Mommy will take Lowell and me downtown for lunch.

I told Mommy, when we have our prayers tonight, let's ask God to turn the rain off and let the sun shine tomorrow. But Mommy says God has a special wonderful way of making rain—he doesn't just turn it on and off.

Daddy got his book and showed me. When the sun shines down hot on rivers and lakes, it picks up drops of water so little you can't see them. They go 'way up in the air till they find some dust. Then they stop on the dust and make a cloud. That's what you see floating around in the sky. Some day when a cold wind blows the cloud, it makes the little drops of water fall back down to the ground again. That's rain.

That's more of God's laws. He always does it that way. And he doesn't change around for me even if I do want to go downtown. If he changed every time somebody wanted it to rain or not to rain, things would get all mixed up.

Rain always stops some time. If you live in a place where there are lots and lots of clouds that let down too much water sometimes and make a flood, then you have to build your house up high. And you have to build walls along the river to keep the water from running over.

If it does stop raining by tomorrow, I'll be glad.

52 WE'RE SORRY

It was hot in our room today. We weren't very good. Chucky and Hughy hit each other. Joan threw doll dishes at Judy and me. Jay turned the piano stool over.

Mrs. Gordon didn't feel happy. Sunday school isn't fun if people are bad. I guess God didn't feel very happy either. Mrs. Gordon told him. When we were ready to go home, she said, "Dear God, we know you're sorry we forgot to be kind. Help us to remember."

Joyce doesn't have a two-wheeler yet. But she has a new baby sister! She says she'd *rather* have a baby sister than a bike. When I tell her to do something, she says, "I don't have to. I have a baby sister and you haven't."

I like to go in her house and see Diane. She's a cute little baby. Her mother isn't always cleaning house now.

Mommy says maybe sometime we'll get a baby sister.

Grandma Janson got dead. The one we sent our Easter flower to. Waldo told us as soon as he came to Sunday school. They're going to put her in the ground. Waldo said so. We asked Mrs. Gordon why.

She told us. Grandma Janson was old and tired. Her hands and eyes and legs were worn out. So God is letting her rest. She doesn't need her old body any more. That's what "dead" is.

But the part of her that liked our Easter flower isn't dead. The part of her that loved Waldo isn't dead. God is still taking care of her.

53 GOING FOR A WALK

Today we left our kindergarten room and took a walk. We saw lots of things. We stood under a tree and looked at the clouds through the leaves. We saw a mother and a father robin scolding 'cause they didn't want us to get too close to their baby birds. We went past Mrs. Spencer's house and saw her roses. Mrs. Gordon thinks it's nice for Mrs. Spencer to have pretty roses for other people to see. Now there are some roses in our part of Rose Park.

There was a wind. It blew on our faces. It pushed us. We couldn't see it. But we could feel it. We knew it was there. Just like God.

And you know what—I said, "Thank you, God," inside myself, without shutting my eyes, and with my head looking up! You can talk to God any way you feel like!

Mrs. Gordon said maybe we'd find some more pretty flowers. But you know what, the police car came by, and the policeman asked us would we like to come see the police station! We all said yes!

Mrs. Gordon whispered to Mommy, "It isn't what I'd planned—but it's a good idea." Mommy nodded.

It was fun going to the police station. The policeman let the boys wear his cap. He showed us how he talks to other policemen a long way off. He told us how to cross streets and ride two-wheelers. And if we ever get lost, tell a policeman.

We liked the policeman so well that now we're going to learn about some other helpers.

KINDERGARTEN IS IMPORTANT

[54]

We're writing a story about helpers. We tell Mrs. Gordon what to write. It's about a boy named Freddy who goes around to visit the helpers. He asks them what they do and they tell him.

Gail and I said to her mother, let's act it out with stick puppets like we use at everyday kindergarten.

The little children at Sunday school who are only four like to make their helpers out of clay and play with them. Some of us older ones are cutting out pictures of helpers and pasting them on cardboard. Then we fasten them on to rulers. They're stick puppets.

Some are painting the scenery on a great big piece of thick cardboard. They paste pictures on too—a police car and a fire engine and a milk truck and things like that.

The big cardboard goes up on the wall. Then right in front of it we'll have two card tables with a blanket hanging down in front. The ones of us who work the puppets hide under the tables.

Mrs. Gordon will read our story, and when it comes to our part, we hold our puppets up against the big cardboard. The people in front can't see us. I'm the carpenter puppet. I walk him right along the black line Miss Cora marked. The puppet pictures are the same on both sides, so we just turn our rulers over and walk our puppets off the same way they came on.

Chucky stays on the board all the time, 'cause he's the boy Freddy. After Freddy talks to each helper, the children who aren't puppets all say, "We give thanks" for milkmen or postmen or garbage men or whatever it is.

We've invited the primary department to come see our play. We think they'll like it. The primary department is where I'll go in a few more Sundays.

We're working so hard! But it's fun.

Roger Block is leaving. He and his mother and daddy are going back to their own house. His daddy doesn't have to go across the ocean again.

126

They gave a present to our kindergarten room. A big picture in a frame—of Jesus talking to the children who went to see him.

I like it the best of any picture. It hangs low where I can touch it. When I go past it, I hold out my hand to Jesus and pretend I am there too.

And guess what! Mommy is happy. Daddy is happy. Mrs. Gordon is happy. Mr. Gordon is happy.

It's on account of the committee Daddy went to this afternoon. Mr. Block found out from little Roger that even kindergarten is important. He wants lots of Sunday-school rooms in the new church now. He doesn't have to have the colored windows. Maybe we'll have a new church in a year!

55 FIRST GRADE

Next Sunday is Promotion. All of us big ones will go to the primary department. Mrs. Gordon took us to see the primary room today. It's not as nice as our room, but I can't keep on being a kindergartner. I'm six years old and in first grade!

I'm glad I can see out of the window one time before I leave the kindergarten. Some of the daddies that had to stand up when they visited our room built a little platform with three steps under the window. It's long enough for Joan and Chucky and Gail and me all to stand on and look out the window. Today I saw a bird fly by.

This morning Mrs. Gordon gave each of us big ones a little book she made. It has a picture of the whole kindergarten that Roger's daddy took. It tells the Bible verses and prayers we like. All the teachers wrote their names in it. It's to keep so we'll always remember kindergarten.

You know what, now there are going to be two kindergartens and two nursery departments and two primary departments, 'cause there are so many children. One like always and one during church—even if the people upstairs do hear us singing. Now there will be real Sunday school for the little ones while their mothers and fathers are at church, instead of just playing in the kindergarten room. There will be regular teachers for the church-time nursery instead of first one mother and then another.

Mrs. Gordon will still be the teacher for one kindergarten. And you know who's the teacher of the other one? My mother! Lowell will be in her class. He wants Daddy to be a teacher too. Mommy says that's a good idea!

Now that I'm in first grade, I'll be too busy to write any more books. "Kathy Ann, First-Grader"—that's who I am now. I'm growing up. I like being who I am. I'm glad God thought of letting me be born.

GOOD-BY!